Conten~~ts~~ KU-025-053

Introduction

Everyone's experience of education is different. However, there are a number of valuable skills that underpin our education. These should help us through all areas of our education and future learning in college, at university, at work or in our own time.

What are the Key Skills?

Key Skills are:

- **general skills** – they are used to improve your learning and performance. They are needed in education, work and everyday life

- **essential in education** because they help you to demonstrate and communicate your ideas and knowledge

- **essential in employment** – if you have Key Skills certificates, an employer will feel confident about your ability in specific areas, eg numeracy. Most people will have several jobs during their lifetime. Key Skills are essential to help you to adapt to different types of job and to remain employable during your working life

- **essential in everyday life** because they are the skills you will need repeatedly. You will need to measure, use money, understand information given in tables, graphs, etc.

The Key Skills qualification was made available from September 2000 and is designed to allow students to demonstrate and improve their proficiency in up to six different areas. The three main Key Skills are:

- Communication
- Application of Number
- Information Technology.

Together these make up the Key Skills qualification. The three wider Key Skills are:

- Working with Others
- Improving own Learning and Performance
- Problem Solving.

The first three Key Skills are available at different levels (1 to 5) with each level representing a progression from one to the next. The last three Key Skills are available from Levels 1 to 3.

Key Skills may be obtained from NVQs, GNVQs, GCE AS/A-Levels or the International Baccalaureate. This handbook is concerned with the Application of Number Key Skill at Level 3.

Obtaining your certificates

In order to secure this qualification, you will need to provide evidence, either through specially designated tasks, or through tasks in courses you are already studying. This evidence should then be collected together in a clearly indexed portfolio.

There will be an internal assessment of your portfolio. It will be assessed by your teachers and verified (checked) by the examination board. When your portfolio material reaches a satisfactory standard, it will be signed off by the Standards Moderator (external examiner) and you will receive a Unit Certificate.

You will also need to pass an externally-verified examination, lasting 90 minutes. This is called an External Assessment Instrument (EAI). The test will consist of questions equivalent to Level 7 of the National Curriculum (ie about Grade C GCSE). When you pass an EAI, you receive a Test Certificate.

'Your assignment, should you choose to accept it...'

Using this handbook

This handbook is presented via four main parts:

- *Part 1* explains Application of Number and how you need to apply your number skills.
- *Part 2* explains what is needed for your portfolio in order to obtain your Unit Certificate. It offers a sample assignment to show you how a portfolio can be put together.
- *Part 3* offers revision notes.
- *Part 4* offers a sample examination and advice to help you with the Test Certificate.

In addition, there is a glossary of terms on pages 116 to 118 and a list of useful Web sites on pages 119 and 120.

The tracking calendars, other forms and the sample assignment are differentiated from the rest of the text by the use of a background tint.

The tracking calendars and forms can be downloaded from the Pearson Publishing Web site at http://www.pearsonpublishing.co.uk/publications/extra/, if you wish to use them in your portfolio.

Part 1

The skills

Key Skills: Application of Number

What is this unit about?

This unit is about applying your number skills in a substantial and complex activity. You will need to show that you can:

- plan and interpret information from different sources
- carry out multi-stage tasks
- present your findings, explain results and justify your choice of methods.

'They're lovely, but what do I do with them?'

What you need to know

The following notes tell you what you need to learn and practise to feel confident about applying number skills in your studies, work or other aspects of your life.

In **planning an activity** and **interpreting information**, you need to know how to:

- plan a substantial and complex activity by breaking it down into a series of tasks
- obtain relevant information from different sources, including a large data set (over 50 items), and use this to meet the purpose of your activity

- use estimation to help you plan, multiplying and dividing numbers of any size rounded to one significant figure
- make accurate and reliable observations over time and use suitable equipment to measure in a variety of appropriate units
- read and understand scale drawings, graphs, complex tables and charts
- read and understand ways of writing very large and very small numbers (eg £1.5 billion, 2.4×10^{-3})
- understand and use compound measures (eg speed in kph, pressures in psi, concentrations in ppm)
- choose appropriate methods for obtaining the results you need and justify your choice.

In **carrying out calculations**, you need to know how to:

- show your methods clearly and work to appropriate levels of accuracy; carry out multi-stage calculations with numbers of any size (eg find the results of growth at 8% over three years, find the volume of water in a swimming pool)
- use powers and roots (eg work out interest on £5000 at 5% over three years)
- work out missing angles and sides in right-angled triangles from known sides and angles
- work out proportional change (eg add VAT at 17.5% by multiplying by 1.175)
- work out actual measurements from scale drawings (eg room or site plan, map, workshop drawing) and scale quantities up and down
- work with large data sets (over 50 items), using measures of average and range to compare distributions, and estimate mean, median and range of grouped data
- rearrange and use formulae, equations and expressions (eg formulae in spreadsheets, finance, and area and volume calculations)
- use checking procedures to identify errors in methods and results.

In **interpreting results** and **presenting your findings**, you need to know how to:

- select and use appropriate methods to illustrate findings, show trends and make comparisons
- examine critically, and justify, your choice of methods
- construct and label charts, graphs, diagrams and scale drawings using accepted conventions
- draw appropriate conclusions based on your findings, including how possible sources of error might have affected your results
- explain how your results relate to the purpose of your activity.

What you must do

The following notes describe the skills you must show. All your work for this section will be assessed. You must have evidence that you can do all the things listed on pages 2 and 3.

You must plan and carry through at least one substantial and complex activity that includes tasks for N3.1, N3.2 and N3.3 – these are explained below. They are the criteria which will be referred to throughout this handbook. For example:

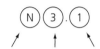

| This means number | This means Level 3 | This means the first section of your work, ie *Planning the activity and interpreting information*. |

Evidence must show you can:

N3.1 – Plan and interpret information from **two** different types of sources, including a large data set.

- *plan how to obtain and use the information required to meet the purpose of your activity*
- *obtain the relevant information*
- *choose appropriate methods for obtaining the results you need and justify your choice.*

N3.2 – Carry out multi-stage calculations to do with:

a   amounts and sizes

b   scales and proportion

c   handling statistics

d   rearranging and using formulae.

You should work with a large data set on at least **one** occasion.

- *carry out calculations to appropriate levels of accuracy, clearly showing your methods*
- *check methods and results to help ensure errors are found and corrected.*

N3.3 – Interpret results of your calculations, present your findings and justify your methods. You must use at least **one** graph, **one** chart and **one** diagram.

- *select appropriate methods of presentation and justify your choice*
- *present your findings effectively*
- *explain how the results of your calculations relate to the purpose of your activity.*

The assignment checklist on pages 28 and 29 can be used to check you have covered all of the tasks for N3.1, N3.2 and N3.3.

Guidance

This section describes some activities you might like to use to develop and show your number skills. It also contains examples of the sort of evidence you could produce to prove you have the skills required.

*'The evidence is in there **somewhere**...'*

You will have opportunities to develop and apply your number skills during your studies, work or other activities. For example, when:

- planning, carrying out and reporting findings from a substantial investigation or project
- designing, making and presenting a product
- researching information and explaining the outcomes to customers or clients.

Your will need time to practise your skills and prepare for assessment. So it is important to plan ahead, for example, to identify an activity that is complex and substantial enough to provide opportunities for following through tasks for N3.1, N3.2 and N3.3. You may need to do additional tasks to cover all the requirements.

Information can be obtained from secondary sources and/or first-hand by measuring or observing. If available, you could use ICT to obtain information from a large database, use spreadsheets and present your findings.

You will need to think about the quality of your Application of Number skills and check your evidence covers all the requirements. The sample assignment on pages 30 to 56 will help you to see what is required.

Examples of evidence include the following:

N3.1 Plan and interpret information:

- A description of the substantial and complex activity and tasks. A plan for obtaining and using the information required.

- Copies of source material, including a note of the large data set and, if applicable, a statement from someone who has checked the accuracy of any measurements or observations.

- Records of the information obtained. A justification of methods selected for achieving the required results.

N3.2 Carry out multi-stage calculations:

- Records of your calculations (for a, b, c and d), showing methods used and levels of accuracy.

- Notes of the large data set used and how you checked methods and results.

N3.3 Interpret results and present findings:

- Report of your findings, including a justification of your presentation methods and explanations of how your results relate to your activity. At least one graph, one chart and one diagram.

- If producing certain types of evidence creates difficulties, due to disability or other factors, you may be able to use other ways to show your achievement. Ask your tutor or supervisor for further information.

Part 2

Your portfolio

Planning your approach

Before you start Year 12

The Application of Number tests are very similar to GCSE Mathematics Intermediate Tier. (This is the examination to gain B or C grades at GCSE.) Therefore, it is a good idea to save all of your Mathematics revision material.

The evidence required for your portfolio may be similar to the coursework projects you did for GCSE Mathematics or Statistics. Make sure that you collect your coursework projects in September from your Maths teacher, as they are likely to be thrown away if you do not. You may be able to reuse them for Application of Number. Also, remember to keep your GCSE Mathematics revision notes as you can use these again when revising for your Test Certificate examination.

Year 12 and 13

The External Assessment Instrument (ie the exam) may be taken at various times during the year. If you obtained Grade C or higher at GCSE, it is wise to take the exam as early as possible before you forget how to do the maths!

Find out the date of your exam. Mark it on the appropriate tracking calendar (see pages 10 to 12). You could plan your revision as follows:

- Eight to 12 weeks before your exam, do two hours revision per week.
- Two to seven weeks before your exam, do three hours revision per week.
- One week before your exam, do one to two hours revision every day.

This handbook contains useful revision notes on pages 57 to 97.

Internal assessment

Internal assessment is the evidence provided by your assignment. This will be signed off by your teachers. You must decide when to do your assignments.

Choice 1: The period between the end of your GCSE exams and the start of Year 12, ie June, July, August.

- ⊕ You have plenty of time.
- ⊕ Years 11 and 13 are not in school. Maths teachers and subject teachers should have more time to help you.
- ⊖ Your teachers may be unwilling to provide suitable assignments before your course starts.
- ⊖ You may want a break from your studies during this time.

Choice 2: June and July of Year 12.

- ⊕ Years 11 and 13 are not in school. Maths teachers should have more time to help you.
- ⊖ You may have important exams, tests, assignments, etc, which need to be done.

Choice 3: During Years 12 and 13.

- ⊕ You can choose appropriate times.
- ⊖ Maths teachers may be busy and unable to give you much help.

Tracking calendars

It is important to keep a clear record of your Key Skills progress. The tracking calendars on pages 10 to 12 allow you to keep a record of the assignments for each element of the Application of Number Key Skill, as well as any exam preparation you may wish to do, etc.

'Trust me, it's a Key Skills assignment!'

To use the tracking calendars, choose a different colour for each of the headings in the key below and fill in the boxes beside them. (If you wish to record other dates or deadlines, etc, you can add them to the key in the spaces provided.) Use the key to colour in the relevant sections of the appropriate tracking calendar. You will then be able to see at a glance when you have to complete your Key Skills work.

Key

Assignment deadlines	☐	Exam preparation	☐
Mock exam dates	☐	Dates of exam	☐
....	☐	....	☐
....	☐	....	☐

When you have completed your Application of Number assignments, you should check that everything has been done. The tracking calendars can be used in conjunction with the tracking sheets on pages 15 and 16, the assessment checklist (pages 25 to 27) and the assignment checklist (pages 28 and 29).

Tracking calendar 2001-2002

	S	S	M	T	W	T	F	S	S	M	T	W	T	F	S	S	M	T	W	T	F	S	S	M	T	W	T	F	S	S	M	T	W	T	F	S	S
SEP	1	2	3	4	5	6	7	8	9	10	11	12	13	14	15	16	17	18	19	20	21	22	23	24	25	26	27	28	29	30							
OCT			1	2	3	4	5	6	7	8	9	10	11	12	13	14	15	16	17	18	19	20	21	22	23	24	25	26	27	28	29	30	31				
NOV						1	2	3	4	5	6	7	8	9	10	11	12	13	14	15	16	17	18	19	20	21	22	23	24	25	26	27	28	29	30		
DEC	1	2	3	4	5	6	7	8	9	10	11	12	13	14	15	16	17	18	19	20	21	22	23	24	25	26	27	28	29	30	31						
JAN				1	2	3	4	5	6	7	8	9	10	11	12	13	14	15	16	17	18	19	20	21	22	23	24	25	26	27	28	29	30	31			
FEB							1	2	3	4	5	6	7	8	9	10	11	12	13	14	15	16	17	18	19	20	21	22	23	24	25	26	27	28			
MAR							1	2	3	4	5	6	7	8	9	10	11	12	13	14	15	16	17	18	19	20	21	22	23	24	25	26	27	28	29	30	31
APR			1	2	3	4	5	6	7	8	9	10	11	12	13	14	15	16	17	18	19	20	21	22	23	24	25	26	27	28	29	30					
MAY					1	2	3	4	5	6	7	8	9	10	11	12	13	14	15	16	17	18	19	20	21	22	23	24	25	26	27	28	29	30	31		
JUN	1	2	3	4	5	6	7	8	9	10	11	12	13	14	15	16	17	18	19	20	21	22	23	24	25	26	27	28	29	30							
JUL			1	2	3	4	5	6	7	8	9	10	11	12	13	14	15	16	17	18	19	20	21	22	23	24	25	26	27	28	29	30	31				
AUG						1	2	3	4	5	6	7	8	9	10	11	12	13	14	15	16	17	18	19	20	21	22	23	24	25	26	27	28	29	30	31	

Tracking calendar 2002-2003

	S	M	T	W	T	F	S	S	M	T	W	T	F	S	S	M	T	W	T	F	S	S	M	T	W	T	F	S	S	M	T	W	T	F	S	S	M	T	W	T	F	S
SEP	1	2	3	4	5	6	7	8	9	10	11	12	13	14	15	16	17	18	19	20	21	22	23	24	25	26	27	28	29	30												
OCT			1	2	3	4	5	6	7	8	9	10	11	12	13	14	15	16	17	18	19	20	21	22	23	24	25	26	27	28	29	30	31									
NOV						1	2	3	4	5	6	7	8	9	10	11	12	13	14	15	16	17	18	19	20	21	22	23	24	25	26	27	28	29	30							
DEC	1	2	3	4	5	6	7	8	9	10	11	12	13	14	15	16	17	18	19	20	21	22	23	24	25	26	27	28	29	30	31											
JAN				1	2	3	4	5	6	7	8	9	10	11	12	13	14	15	16	17	18	19	20	21	22	23	24	25	26	27	28	29	30	31								
FEB							1	2	3	4	5	6	7	8	9	10	11	12	13	14	15	16	17	18	19	20	21	22	23	24	25	26	27	28								
MAR							1	2	3	4	5	6	7	8	9	10	11	12	13	14	15	16	17	18	19	20	21	22	23	24	25	26	27	28	29	30	31					
APR			1	2	3	4	5	6	7	8	9	10	11	12	13	14	15	16	17	18	19	20	21	22	23	24	25	26	27	28	29	30										
MAY					1	2	3	4	5	6	7	8	9	10	11	12	13	14	15	16	17	18	19	20	21	22	23	24	25	26	27	28	29	30	31							
JUN	1	2	3	4	5	6	7	8	9	10	11	12	13	14	15	16	17	18	19	20	21	22	23	24	25	26	27	28	29	30												
JUL			1	2	3	4	5	6	7	8	9	10	11	12	13	14	15	16	17	18	19	20	21	22	23	24	25	26	27	28	29	30	31									
AUG						1	2	3	4	5	6	7	8	9	10	11	12	13	14	15	16	17	18	19	20	21	22	23	24	25	26	27	28	29	30	31						

Tracking calendar 2003-2004

	S	M	T	W	T	F	S	S	M	T	W	T	F	S	S	M	T	W	T	F	S	S	M	T	W	T	F	S	S	M	T	W	T	F	S	S	M
SEP		1	2	3	4	5	6	7	8	9	10	11	12	13	14	15	16	17	18	19	20	21	22	23	24	25	26	27	28	29	30						
OCT				1	2	3	4	5	6	7	8	9	10	11	12	13	14	15	16	17	18	19	20	21	22	23	24	25	26	27	28	29	30	31			
NOV							1	2	3	4	5	6	7	8	9	10	11	12	13	14	15	16	17	18	19	20	21	22	23	24	25	26	27	28	29	30	
DEC		1	2	3	4	5	6	7	8	9	10	11	12	13	14	15	16	17	18	19	20	21	22	23	24	25	26	27	28	29	30	31					
JAN					1	2	3	4	5	6	7	8	9	10	11	12	13	14	15	16	17	18	19	20	21	22	23	24	25	26	27	28	29	30	31		
FEB	1	2	3	4	5	6	7	8	9	10	11	12	13	14	15	16	17	18	19	20	21	22	23	24	25	26	27	28	29								
MAR		1	2	3	4	5	6	7	8	9	10	11	12	13	14	15	16	17	18	19	20	21	22	23	24	25	26	27	28	29	30	31					
APR					1	2	3	4	5	6	7	8	9	10	11	12	13	14	15	16	17	18	19	20	21	22	23	24	25	26	27	28	29	30			
MAY							1	2	3	4	5	6	7	8	9	10	11	12	13	14	15	16	17	18	19	20	21	22	23	24	25	26	27	28	29	30	31
JUN			1	2	3	4	5	6	7	8	9	10	11	12	13	14	15	16	17	18	19	20	21	22	23	24	25	26	27	28	29	30					
JUL					1	2	3	4	5	6	7	8	9	10	11	12	13	14	15	16	17	18	19	20	21	22	23	24	25	26	27	28	29	30	31		
AUG	1	2	3	4	5	6	7	8	9	10	11	12	13	14	15	16	17	18	19	20	21	22	23	24	25	26	27	28	29	30	31						

Planning your portfolio material

Organising your portfolio

Your portfolio must have an index to allow evidence to be found quickly. The following tracking sheets will help your organisation:

- **Tracking sheet 1** (see the example on page 15). A copy of this tracking sheet should be at the start of your Key Skills portfolio.

- **Tracking sheet 2** (see the example on page 16). A copy of this tracking sheet should be at the start of your Application of Number section in your Key Skills portfolio. It should have a list of all assignments (with page references) which contain material you can use for Application of Number.

Assessors will be impressed if they see a well-organised portfolio with an index and tracking sheets which cross-reference work (ie tells the assessor where to find work). Invariably, good organisation means a good candidate with good work.

It is likely that you will have work from a wide range of subjects and Key Skills that will need to be assessed.

In order to organise your work, you will therefore need separate files/folders for each of your main subjects. These files will contain some work for Key Skills.

You need a front cover for each assignment. An example is given on the right.

All assignments must have a reference number to make them easy to find. For example, 'HI1' could indicate your first History assignment.

Name:	
Date:	
Assignment reference number:	
Assignment title:	

Skills contained Key Skills:	Relevant pages
Application of Number	
Communication	
Information Technology	
Working with Others	
Improving own Learning and Presentation	
Problem Solving	

Types of evidence

You should use evidence of Application of Number from a wide range of subjects. Types of evidence for your portfolio include:

- original work
- photocopies
- page/assignment references to work elsewhere in your portfolio (ie tracking sheets)
- reports
- documents
- video and audio cassettes
- presentation slides
- spreadsheets.

Remember that it is the **quality** of your assignments that counts, not the **quantity**.

Application of Number material **must** have a purpose, ie it must form part of your studies with explanations of the purpose of your calculations and justification of your methods. Maths questions or exercises from GCSE textbooks are **not** acceptable as evidence.

*'These are the best value for money – and I can **prove** it...'*

If possible, choose one or two assignments from your main studies which contain considerable material for Application of Number. (A sample assignment is shown on pages 30 to 56.) This will allow you to use the same material twice; once for your main subject and once for Key Skills Application of Number.

Tracking sheet 1

Assignment reference
number or title
(ie where it can be found)

	Application of Number	Communication	Information Technology	Working with Others	Improving own Learning and Performance	Problem Solving
	☐	☐	☐	☐	☐	☐
	☐	☐	☐	☐	☐	☐
	☐	☐	☐	☐	☐	☐
	☐	☐	☐	☐	☐	☐
	☐	☐	☐	☐	☐	☐
	☐	☐	☐	☐	☐	☐
	☐	☐	☐	☐	☐	☐
	☐	☐	☐	☐	☐	☐
	☐	☐	☐	☐	☐	☐
	☐	☐	☐	☐	☐	☐
	☐	☐	☐	☐	☐	☐
	☐	☐	☐	☐	☐	☐
	☐	☐	☐	☐	☐	☐
	☐	☐	☐	☐	☐	☐
	☐	☐	☐	☐	☐	☐
	☐	☐	☐	☐	☐	☐
	☐	☐	☐	☐	☐	☐
	☐	☐	☐	☐	☐	☐
	☐	☐	☐	☐	☐	☐
	☐	☐	☐	☐	☐	☐
	☐	☐	☐	☐	☐	☐
	☐	☐	☐	☐	☐	☐

Tracking sheet 2

Assignment reference number or title (ie where it can be found)	Page number or section	Material/work for Application of Number

Your assignment

What is required?

Your assignment – this may be called evidence, project, coursework, activity – will be part of your portfolio. An explanation of the code letters and numbers is given on page 4.

You must use at least one graph, one chart or one diagram for each assignment.

You will be required to produce at least one (probably two) assignments for Application of Number.

The assignments should be related to your main studies, eg if you are taking A-level Business Studies you could use a study of your school mini-company to provide the information for your Application of Number assignment.

The assignment you will do for Application of Number will be similar to your GCSE Mathematics coursework projects.

In your assignment you will be expected to:

- choose a project (or your teacher may set an assignment)
- obtain information
- use the information
- demonstrate your mathematical ability and perform calculations (the revision notes on pages 57 to 97 will help you with this)
- draw graphs, charts and diagrams
- present the results of your calculations.

Reactions to his Etchosketch presentation were mixed...

A blank assignment checklist is provided on pages 28 and 29. This shows you what is needed in your project. Tick the appropriate boxes as you do your assignment then you will know what has been done and what you need to do. This should be used in conjunction with the assessment checklist on pages 25 to 27.

If you want to complete the Application of Number course with one assignment, you must tick every box from A to V (see the assignment checklist, pages 28 and 29).

You may find that you need to do two assignments to tick all of the boxes. If so, you must tick every box from A to K for each assignment and you must tick every box from L to V for at least one of your assignments.

Sample assignment

A sample assignment is shown on pages 30 to 56 (indicated by a tinted background). A general assignment has been provided to show what is expected. (Alternatively, you may wish to prepare a subject-specific assignment.) This assignment is suitable for any subject and can be easily supervised and marked by a Mathematics teacher. It shows how to plan the assignment and also shows a variety of mathematical techniques, diagrams, graphs, etc, which may be useful for inclusion in your own assignment. Note that within the sample assignment, page 30 shows what is being done in the assignment and page 31 shows what you can claim to have covered. The circled letters at the top of the pages in the sample assignment refer to what you can claim on the assignment checklist (pages 33 and 34).

*"Could you just mark **these**... ?"*

Stage 1: Getting started

(You are advised to read pages 19 to 29 and look at the sample assignment on pages 30 to 56 before starting your Application of Number assignment.)

Your teacher may suggest a suitable assignment. If not, you will have to choose your own.

Select an assignment, preferably from your main studies. This will allow you to use it for Application of Number **and** your main studies. Make sure that it will allow you to demonstrate your mathematical ability.

Discuss your intention to use the project for Application of Number with your subject teacher (if it is a Geography project, ask your Geography teacher) **and** the Mathematics teacher who is supervising Application of Number.

If either of your teachers is unsure or discouraging, think of another assignment. Do **not** waste time on an assignment which may be unsuitable. If **both** teachers think it is suitable, move to stage 2.

'Hello Sir, thought of an assignment yet?'

Stage 2: Is there enough mathematics in the project?

Before you spend lots of time on the assignment, you must be sure that it will produce the mathematics you require.

In one of your projects you must use a **primary** source of data, ie data you collect yourself (eg questionnaires, observation, experiment):

- **Questionnaire** – There is an example on pages 35 to 37.
- **Observation** – Something you observe (eg you could count the number of cars, lorries and buses as part of a traffic survey).
- **Experiment** – You collect data by setting up an experiment (eg you could carry out a fitness experiment by taking pulse rates before and after exercise).

In one of your assignments you must use a **secondary** source of data, ie data provided by someone else (eg from books, statistical tables, the Internet, or government statistics which are often found in the reference section in libraries).

In one of your assignments you must use a large data set of over 50 items. For example, you could take the pulse rates of 60 people. The large data set can be primary data (collected by you) or secondary data (collected by someone else, eg data in books). It will be easier to use the data if it is numerical rather than opinions. For example, for the question "How tall are you?", the answer will be numerical and easy to use, eg 172 cm, 180 cm, 152 cm, etc. But if the question is "What is your favourite colour?", the answer will not be numerical. The data will be much more difficult to use. For example, blue, red, green, blue, etc.

*He'd found a **few** secondary sources...*

Stage 3: Does your assignment include multi-stage calculations?

In your assignment (or assignments) you must produce multi-stage calculations in the following:

- Amounts and sizes, eg working with measures such as length, weight, capacity, mass (weight), time, money, very large and very small numbers.

  The following is an example of a multi-stage calculation:

  You could do a traffic survey to calculate the speed of cars and how many break the speed limit.

  1. Measure a distance, say 100 m.
  2. Find how many seconds cars take to travel this distance.
  3. Use time and distance to calculate the speed in kilometres per hour.
  4. Convert the speed in kilometres per hour into miles per hour.

- Scales and proportion, eg scale diagrams and ratio.
- Handling statistics, eg using data and statistics.
- Rearranging and using formulae, eg $°F = \frac{9}{5}°C + 32$.

  Rewrite the formulae to make °C the subject, ie $°C = \frac{5}{9}(°F - 32)$.

  You could then use the formula to convert 68°F into °C.

*He decided that an abacus was not
ideal for multi-stage calculations...*

Using ICT

Your assignment provides an ideal way to use Information and Communication Technology (ICT).

ICT can be used for your graphs and diagrams. It will allow you to present information in attractive visual form. However, you must always justify your choice of graph. The information provided must be **meaningful**. Don't use a computer image unless it shows the data in a clear, easy-to-understand form.

Checking accuracy

If you use Information and Communication Technology to produce graphs, diagrams and charts, you must fully explain them and check their accuracy.

Suppose you use ICT to produce a pie chart, you must also show how to calculate the angles at the centre of the pie chart (see page 97).

Checking your work

You must show evidence of checking your work. This can be difficult. You should use either method 1 or 2.

Method 1

If you check your work and find an error, write 'Error found' on the side of the paper.

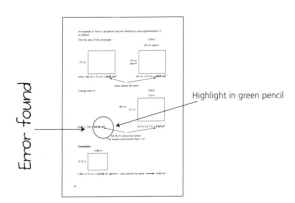

Highlight in green pencil

Highlight the error in coloured pencil.

Add an extra page at this point in your assignment explaining how you found your error and corrected it.

See page 47 of the sample assignment for an example.

Method 2

If you check your work and find an error, rewrite the page with the correct maths. Put a note saying 'See Appendix A'.

Add an appendix (ie a short section at the end of your assignment) entitled 'Errors'. In the 'Errors' appendix place all of your mistakes and explain how you checked, found and corrected them.

You must also check by using approximation. This section should be called 'Checking procedures'. You must show a couple of checks for each section, ie:

a   amounts and sizes

b   scales and proportion

c   handling statistics

d   rearranging and using formulae

He was carefully checking his work!

23

An example of how a calculation may be checked by using approximation is as follows:

Find the area of this rectangle.   Check

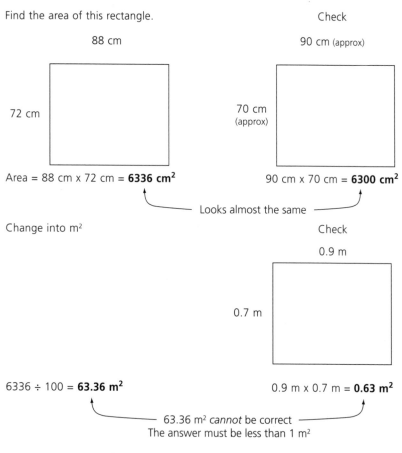

88 cm   90 cm (approx)

72 cm   70 cm (approx)

Area = 88 cm x 72 cm = **6336 cm²**   90 cm x 70 cm = **6300 cm²**

Looks almost the same

Change into m²   Check

0.9 m

0.7 m

6336 ÷ 100 = **63.36 m²**   0.9 m x 0.7 m = **0.63 m²**

63.36 m² *cannot* be correct
The answer must be less than 1 m²

Correction

0.88 m

0.72 m

0.88 x 0.72 m = **0.6336 m²** ←——— Looks almost the same ———→ **0.63 m²**

Assessment checklist

Fill in this sheet as you do your assignment. (This should be used in conjunction with the assignment checklist, pages 28 and 29.)

N3.1 Plan and interpret information from two different types of sources, including a large data set.

Tick when done

- Have you chosen a complex activity?
  (See the sample assignment page 30.) ☐

- Have you broken the complex activity into a series of connected tasks? (See the plan page 30.) ☐

- Are these tasks sequenced clearly? ie Have you shown the order of the tasks? ☐

- Have you explained what should be done first and why? ☐

- Have you made use of earlier information and calculations in later tasks? ☐

- Is there a clear description of each task? ☐

- Have you given reasons for choosing your tasks? ☐

- Have you explained how you obtain information? ☐

- Do your tasks include:

  - Obtaining information from a primary source?
    (ie information you obtain yourself from a survey, observation, experiment, etc) ☐

  - Obtaining information from a secondary source?
    (ie information found by someone else. The information could be found from books, tables, graphs, the Internet, libraries, etc.) ☐

  - Using a large data set of over 50 items? ☐

N3.2 Carry out multi-stage calculations to do with:

a   **amounts and sizes**

b   **scales and proportions**

c   **handling statistics**

d   **rearranging and using formulae.**

You must work with a large data set on at least one occasion.

Tick when done

• Have you done some calculations using:

a   amounts and sizes, eg powers, square roots, finding angles and sides, measurements, large and small numbers, etc?   ☐

b   scales and proportion, eg ratio, scale drawings, etc?   ☐

c   handling statistics, eg frequency charts, histograms, calculating mean, median, range, comparing two sets of data, etc?   ☐

d   rearranging and using formulae, eg solving simultaneous equations, using formulae such as area of a circle = πr^2. Changing the subject of a formula.   ☐

• Have you checked calculations by approximating to one significant figure, eg check 27 x 71 = 1917 by doing 30 x 70 = 2100?   ☐

• Have you worked to appropriate levels of accuracy, eg when calculating the area of a room working to the nearest 10 cm is accurate enough for length and width?   ☐

• Have you done some multi-stage calculations, ie used the results from one stage to do other calculations? For example, measure the length and width of eight rooms and then use the areas of the rooms to find the mean average floor area.   ☐

N3.3 Interpret results of your calculations, present your findings and justify your methods. You must use at least one graph, one chart and one diagram.

Tick when done

- Have you justified the methods you have used? ie explained what you have done and why you have done it. ☐

- Have you explained the reasons for doing calculations? (ie what you are trying to do) ☐

- Have you explained your results and what they show? (For example, have you explained the purpose of the calculations you have done in relation to the assignment? Have you explained how the calculations meet the purpose of the assignment?) ☐

- Have you drawn some graphs? (At least one drawn by hand with calculations shown.) ☐

- Have you drawn some charts? (At least one drawn by hand with calculations shown.) ☐

- Have you drawn some diagrams? (At least one drawn by hand with calculations shown.) ☐

- You should include some of these: graphs, flow chart, bar chart, pie chart, histogram, frequency polygon, scatter diagram, network diagram, scale drawings, cumulative frequency diagram, conversion graph. ☐

- Have you used Information and Communication Technology (ICT) to produce some graphs? You must fully explain your diagrams and check their accuracy. ☐

Assignment checklist

Candidate's name:	
Title:	
Portfolio reference/page number:	Centre:
Assignment 1:	
Assignment 2:	

Every box must have an entry tick (or page reference) to show it has been done.

	Assignment 1	Assignment 2	Teacher's Initials
N3.1 Plan and interpret information			
A Plan how to obtain and use the information required to meet the purpose of your activity	☐	☐	
B Obtain the relevant information	☐	☐	
C Choose appropriate methods for obtaining the results you need and justify your choice	☐	☐	
N3.2 Carry out multi-stage calculations			
D Carry out calculations to appropriate levels of accuracy, clearly showing your methods	☐	☐	
L Amounts and sizes	☐	☐	
N Scales and proportions	☐	☐	
P Handling statistics	☐	☐	
R Rearranging and using formulae	☐	☐	
E Check methods and results to help ensure errors are found and corrected	☐	☐	
M Amounts and sizes	☐	☐	
O Scales and proportions	☐	☐	
Q Handling statistics	☐	☐	
S Rearranging and using formulae	☐	☐	

N3.3 Interpret results of your calculations, present your findings and justify your methods

	Assignment 1	Assignment 2	Teacher's Initials
F Select appropriate methods of presentation and justify your choice	☐	☐	
G Present your findings effectively	☐	☐	
H Explain how the results of your calculations relate to the purpose of your activity	☐	☐	
I Use a graph	☐	☐	
J Use a chart	☐	☐	
K Use a diagram	☐	☐	

Which assignment contains: *(tick one box only for each item)*

	Assignment 1	Assignment 2	Teacher's Initials
T A data set with more than 50 items of data	☐	☐	
U A primary data source (found by *your* questionnaire, measurements, etc)	☐	☐	
V A secondary data source (from books, the Internet, etc)	☐	☐	

Confirmation that all aspects of Application of Number are complete:

Candidate's signature:

Teacher's signature:

Print name:

Date:

Sample assignment

> "A proposal has been made to convert a classroom into a computer suite for use by sixth form classes (not private study)." Investigate the school's needs and suggest suitable classrooms.

Plan

1 Conduct a survey. Produce a short questionnaire. Ask over 50 teachers. (If there were less than 50 teachers, the survey would need to be changed and students' opinions found.)

2 Use the data from the questionnaire to find the optimum size for the new computer room, ie number of computers needed.

3 Obtain details of sixth form classes from a secondary source.

4 Analyse quality of existing computer rooms.

5 Try to find a relationship between the number of computers in a room and the floor space. (If there are less than six computer rooms in the school it will be necessary to obtain data from computer rooms at other schools.)

6 Choose a room.

7 Draw a scale diagram of a typical 'footprint'. The 'footprint' is the table space occupied by the tower, monitor, keyboard, mouse pad, speakers, etc.

8 Diagram of the computer room.

The letters in the circles (eg **B**) refer to the boxes you can tick on the assignment checklist (see pages 33 and 34).

You need a title for your assignment.

A plan is needed. This must show: **A** *30*

- What information is required.
- How the information will be obtained.
- How the information will be used.

1
- Use a survey to obtain results.   **B** **C** *35 to 37*
- Design a questionnaire (justify your choice).   **C** *35 to 37*
- Obtain data from over 50 people (large data set).   **T** *37 and 38*
- You collected this data (primary data).   **U** *37 and 38*
- Present data in a table.   **G** *37*

2
- Present data in a table.   **G** *38*
- Show information in a cumulative frequency diagram. **F** **G** **K** *38 to 41*
- Analyse data using median, quartiles, etc.   **D** **P** **Q** *39 and 40*
- Present findings and justify use of cumulative frequency diagram.   **F** **H** *40 and 41*

3
- Work with more than 50 items of data.   **T** *42*
- Secondary data used.   **V** *42*
- Class sizes from computer-generated lists (secondary data) compared with information from questionnaire.   **P** **Q** *43 and 44*
- Graphs (histogram, frequency polygon).   **G** **I** *43*
- Pie chart, analyse results, justify choice.   **F** **G** **J** *44*

4
- Table to present data.   **G** **L** **M** *45*
- Analysis of data.   **G** **H** *46*

5
- Measure existing computer rooms .   **A** **B** **C** *46*
- Calculate space needed for each computer.   **D** **L** *47*
- Check working.   **E** **M** *47*
- Calculations and checking.   **D** **E** **L** **M** *47 and 48*
- Scatter diagram, formula.   **E** **G** **I** **L** **M** **R** *49*
- Using formulae.   **D** **E** **H** **R** **S** *50*
- Conversion graphs.   **F** **G** **I** *51*
- Calculations.   **G** **H** **L** **M** *52*

6
- Reasons given for choice.   *52*

7
- Scale drawing.   **K** **L** **N** *53*

8
- Plan for designing the computer room.   **A** *54*
- Scale drawing, ratio.   **F** **G** **K** **N** **O** *55 and 56*

Possible extensions to the assignment

Ideas include:

- Cost of equipment. Could include VAT, percentages, minimum and maximum cost, estimation, etc.

- Painting walls and ceiling. Cost of paint, area of walls and ceiling. Time required, etc. Flooring, cost of tiles, area of tiles in cm^2 and floor area in m^2.

- Further questionnaire.

- More statistics – graphs, charts, diagrams.

- If you have not used secondary data, ie data obtained from books, the Internet, statistical tables, etc, you will need to do this. You could try health and safety, insurance companies or computer firms to find out the maximum amount of people and equipment that can be put in a room and still meet health and safety regulations.

Assignment checklist

Candidate's name: CAROLYN McLOUGHLIN	
Title: Numeracy	
Portfolio reference/page number: NUM1	**Centre:** 12345
Assignment 1: Designing a computer room	
Assignment 2: N/A	

Every box must have an entry tick (or page reference) to show it has been done.

	Assignment 1	Assignment 2	Teacher's Initials
N3.1 Plan and interpret information			
A Plan how to obtain and use the information required to meet the purpose of your activity	✓	☐	*SB*
B Obtain the relevant information	✓	☐	*SB*
C Choose appropriate methods for obtaining the results you need and justify your choice	✓	☐	*SB*
N3.2 Carry out multi-stage calculations			
D Carry out calculations to appropriate levels of accuracy, clearly showing your methods	✓	☐	*SB*
L Amounts and sizes	✓	☐	*SB*
N Scales and proportions	✓	☐	*SB*
P Handling statistics	✓	☐	*SB*
R Rearranging and using formulae	✓	☐	*SB*
E Check methods and results to help ensure errors are found and corrected	✓	☐	*SB*
M Amounts and sizes	✓	☐	*SB*
O Scales and proportions	✓	☐	*SB*
Q Handling statistics	✓	☐	*SB*
S Rearranging and using formulae	✓	☐	*SB*

N3.3 Interpret results of your calculations, present your findings and justify your methods

	Assignment 1	Assignment 2	Teacher's Initials
F Select appropriate methods of presentation and justify your choice	☑	☐	SB
G Present your findings effectively	☑	☐	SB
H Explain how the results of your calculations relate to the purpose of your activity	☑	☐	SB
I Use a graph	☑	☐	SB
J Use a chart	☑	☐	SB
K Use a diagram	☑	☐	SB

Which assignment contains: *(tick one box only for each item)*

	Assignment 1	Assignment 2	Teacher's Initials
T A data set with more than 50 items of data	☑	☐	SB
U A primary data source (found by *your* questionnaire, measurements, etc)	☑	☐	SB
V A secondary data source (from books, the Internet, etc)	☑	☐	SB

Confirmation that all aspects of Application of Number are complete:

Candidate's signature: Carolyn McLoughlin

Teacher's signature: Stafford Burndred

Print name: STAFFORD BURNDRED

Date: 7/5/01

Questionnaire

A starting point is required for the assignment. A good way to do this is to conduct a survey to find opinions. (A questionnaire is a primary data source.)

The survey will:

a find out if a computer room is needed for sixth form classes

b find the number of computer stations required in the room

c assess the quality of the existing computer rooms.

Firstly, write the questionnaire and then use it with a few friends (known as a pilot). If any questions are difficult to answer or understand, they may need to be rewritten.

Ways of conducting the questionnaire

Hand out questionnaires for teachers to fill in and return.

- **Advantage:** Quick and easy.
- **Disadvantage:** Response rate may be low. People will lose the questionnaire, forget to return it or throw it away.

Ask teachers to answer a few quick questions. (The survey needs to be short to allow each person to respond in a couple of minutes.)

- **Advantage:** Ensures responses and if a question is difficult to understand, the interviewer can clarify the question.

'Shall I explain the question to you, Sir?'

Questionnaire

1 a Do you think that an additional computer suite for sixth form classes is required? Yes/No

   b Have you seen or used the computers in all of rooms 1, 18, 27, 30, 42, 48? (provide map) Yes/No

If anyone responds 'No' to either of the above, ask no more questions. Do not use their data.

2 A new computer room is planned for use with sixth form classes only. How many computers would you like to have in the room?

   a minimum number

   b desired number.

3 There are six computer rooms in the school. Comment upon your opinion of the room for sixth form classes. [Provide map showing the location of the rooms.] (The map was provided because in the pilot survey some teachers did not know the computer room numbers.)

Room	Opinion			
	Excellent	Good	Satisfactory	Poor
1	☐	☐	☐	☐
18	☐	☐	☐	☐
27	☐	☐	☐	☐
30	☐	☐	☐	☐
42	☐	☐	☐	☐
48	☐	☐	☐	☐

The data collection sheet on page 37 uses the following abbreviations:

EX = Excellent

GD = Good

 S = Satisfactory

 P = Poor.

Data collection sheet for questionnaire

B G T U

Room 48				Room 42				Room 30				Room 27				Room 18				Room 1				Q3	2b	Q2a	Name
P	S	GD	EX	P	S	GD	EX	P	S	GD	EX	P	S	GD	EX	P	S	GD	EX	P	S	GD	EX				
	✓				✓					✓				✓				✓						✓	18	12	Miss Grey
	✓						✓		✓					✓					✓			✓		✓	18	8	Mr Jones
	✓						✓				✓			✓				✓						✓	12	12	Mr Smith
✓					✓				✓					✓				✓						✓	20	20	Mr Brown
	✓						✓		✓			✓						✓						✓	20	20	Mr White
	✓						✓		✓					✓			✓							✓	28	18	Miss Andrews
✓							✓		✓					✓					✓					✓	20	6	Mrs Green
✓							✓		✓					✓					✓					✓	12	4	Mrs Prentice
✓					✓					✓		✓				✓								✓	24	15	Mr Roberts
✓				✓				✓					✓					✓						✓	22	22	Miss Campbell
	✓				✓				✓					✓				✓						✓	18	10	Mrs Wilson
		✓					✓		✓					✓					✓					✓	21	12	Mr James
✓					✓						✓	✓						✓						✓	17	12	Miss Cross
	✓				✓					✓				✓					✓					✓	19	19	Miss Randall
	✓						✓	✓						✓				✓						✓	16	16	Mr Weston
✓							✓			✓					✓			✓						✓	12	6	Mrs Bell
✓							✓		✓						✓			✓						✓	14	6	Mr Machin
✓							✓		✓				✓						✓			✓		✓	13	10	Mr Payne
	✓				✓			✓					✓					✓						✓	19	19	Ms Benn
		✓			✓						✓		✓					✓						✓	30	24	Mrs Riley
9	9	2	0	0	0	1	9	10	0	3	9	8	0	4	14	2	0	2	10	8	0	0	5	15	373	271	TOTAL

37

Data collection table results

Page 37 shows the results from 20 teachers. A total of 78 teachers took part in the survey. 18 stated that an additional computer room was not needed or they had not used all of the rooms. They were not asked to answer any further questions.

The results for the 60 teachers who answered 'Yes' to both parts of Question 1 are as follows:

(See page 39 to show how cumulative frequency is calculated.)

Question 2a responses

Minimum number of computers	Frequency	Cumulative frequency
0–5	3	3
6–10	10	13
11–15	16	29
16–20	18	47
21–25	10	57
26–30	3	60

Question 2b responses

Desired number of computers	Frequency	Cumulative frequency
0–5	0	0
6–10	0	0
11–15	13	13
16–20	31	44
21–25	9	53
26–30	7	60

This data can be shown in a cumulative frequency diagram (see pages 39 and 40).

Cumulative frequency diagram to show the minimum number of computers required for the new computer room.

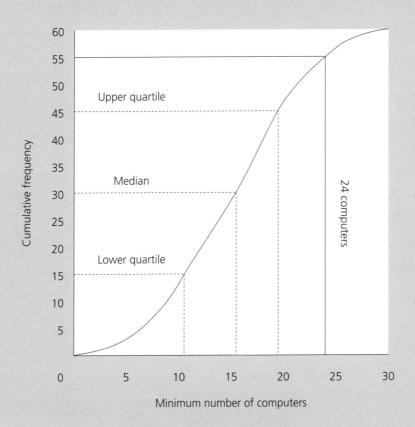

- Upper quartile 19.5 computers
- Median 15.5 computers
- Lower quartile 10.5 computers

The cumulative frequency graph shows that 55 teachers out of 60 thought that the minimum number of computers was 24 or less.

55/60 = 91⅔%

Therefore, if the new computer room has 24 computers, this will satisfy 'the minimum number of computers' for 91⅔% of the teachers.

If the new computer room has 20 computers, this will satisfy 'the minimum number of computers' for over 75% of the teachers.

Cumulative frequency diagram to show the desired number of computers for the new computer room.

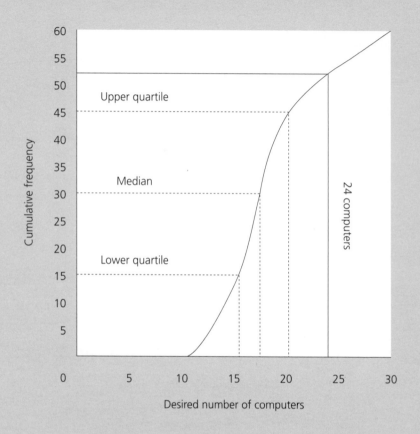

- Upper quartile 20.5 computers
- Median 17.5 computers
- Lower quartile 15.5 computers

The cumulative frequency graph shows that 52 teachers out of 60 thought that the desired number of computers was 24 or less.

52/60 = 86⅔%

Therefore, if the new computer room has 24 computers, this will satisfy 'the desired number of computers' for 86⅔% of the teachers.

If the new computer room has 21 computers, this will satisfy 'the desired number of computers' for over 75% of the teachers.

Reasons for using a cumulative frequency diagram

The diagram provides a relationship between the number of computers in a room and the number of teachers who will be satisfied (minimum number of computers) or pleased (desired number of computers in the room).

This will facilitate the task of finding a suitable number of computers to satisfy/please the majority of teachers.

A good measure is the upper quartile. If the number of computers exceeds this, it will ensure that a minimum of 75% of the teachers will be satisfied/pleased.

Findings from the cumulative frequency diagram

Some teachers desired 30 computers, but it will be less expensive in money and space to have less. A compromise is needed to satisfy most teachers and keep costs down.

21 computers will please over 75% of the teachers. Therefore rooms which will not accommodate 21 computers will be rejected.

24 computers would satisfy the requirements of over 90% of teachers. Therefore, a room which will accommodate 24 computers is preferred.

Sixth form class sizes

Large costs are involved in equipping the computer room. Teachers have given their opinions about students who need to be accommodated. It makes sense to obtain actual class sizes for the lower sixth. (This will allow working with a large set of secondary data.)

A printout of all Year 12 classes was obtained. (Note if a class has five lessons in a week, only one class list was produced.) You should include some of these class lists in the appendix.

The following information was extracted by counting names on each list.

Class size	Tally	Frequency
3	I	1
8	I	1
9	I	1
10	II	2
11	I	1
12	II	2
13		0
14	IIII II	7
15	IIII	4
16	IIII III	8
17	IIII I	6
18	IIII IIII	9
19	IIII I	6
20	IIII	4
21	III	3
22	III	3
23	III	3
24	IIII	4
25	I	1
26	I	1
27	II	2
28	I	1
29	I	1
Total		71

If the computer room can accommodate 24 students, this will be large enough for 65 out of 71 classes, ie 91.5% of classes.

The information from the questionnaire gives very similar results, ie $86\frac{2}{3}$% of teachers stated that the desired number of computers was 24 or less (ie information obtained from cumulative frequency diagram)

and

$91\frac{2}{3}$% of teachers stated that the minimum number of computers was 24 or less (ie information obtained from cumulative frequency diagrams).

The information from the primary data (survey) is in strong agreement with the information from the secondary data (sixth form class sizes).

Sixth form class size

Class sizes for lower sixth

Class size	0–4	5–9	10–14	11–19	20–24	25–29	30–34
Frequency	1	2	12	33	17	6	0

The information can be shown more clearly on a histogram.

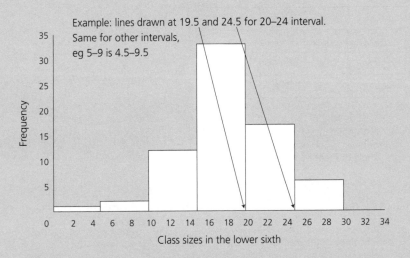

Example: lines drawn at 19.5 and 24.5 for 20–24 interval.
Same for other intervals,
eg 5–9 is 4.5–9.5

It can also be shown in a frequency polygon.

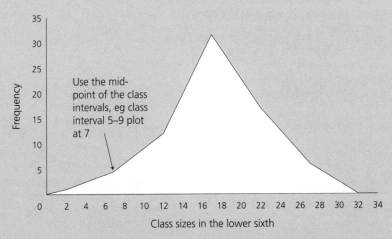

Use the mid-point of the class intervals, eg class interval 5–9 plot at 7

43

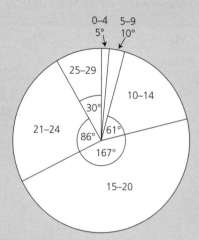

Class interval	Frequency	Multiply by	Angle at centre of circle
0–4	1	$360/71$	5°
5–9	2	$360/71$	10°
10–14	12	$360/71$	61°
11–19	33	$360/71$	167°
20–24	17	$360/71$	86°
25–29	6	$360/71$	30°
30–34	0	$360/71$	0°

Adds up to 359° because all numbers have been rounded to the nearest whole number

Pie chart to show class sizes for the lower sixth

A pie chart is able to show information visually and is much clearer than in tabular form.

The lower pie chart shows clearly that 24 computers will be sufficient to accommodate the majority of sixth form classes.

The information from the sixth form class lists (secondary data) is in agreement with the information from the questionnaire (primary data).

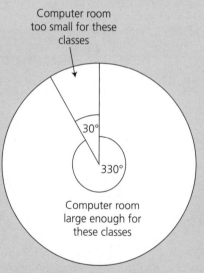

Pie chart to show lower sixth class sizes which can and cannot be catered for by the computer room if it has 24 computers

Before finding a relationship between the number of computers in a room and the floor area required, the responses to question 3 should be analysed. This may help to identify good and bad computer rooms.

Question 3

G L M

To simplify the analysis of the results, a response of excellent = 5 points, good = 3 points, satisfactory = 1 point. (The results for the first 20 teachers are given on page 37.) These are the results from the 60 teachers.

					Rank order	Number of computers
Room 1	Excellent	47	x 5	235		
	Good	13	x 3	39		
	Satisfactory	0	x 1	0		
	Poor	0		Total = 274	1	36
Room 18	Excellent	20	x 5	100		
	Good	26	x 3	78		
	Satisfactory	4	x 1	4		
	Poor	0		Total = 182	4	6
Room 27	Excellent	3	x 5	15		
	Good	39	x 3	117		
	Satisfactory	17	x 1	17		
	Poor	1		Total = 149	5	24
Room 30	Excellent	26	x 5	130		
	Good	23	x 3	69		
	Satisfactory	11	x 1	11		
	Poor	0		Total = 210	3	30
Room 42	Excellent	32	x 5	160		
	Good	25	x 3	75		
	Satisfactory	3	x 1	3		
	Poor	0		Total = 238	2	8
Room 48	Excellent	0	x 5	0		
	Good	5	x 3	15		
	Satisfactory	25	x 1	25		
	Poor	30		Total = 40	6	24

45

Analysis

Room 1 with 36 computers was ranked first.

Room 42 with 8 computers was ranked second.

Room 48 with 24 computers was ranked sixth.

This suggests no relationship between the opinions that teachers had of computer rooms (ie excellent, good, satisfactory, poor) and the number of computers.

This was surprising. If time permitted, it would be advantageous to find reasons for teachers' preferences.

Options could be:

- A more detailed questionnaire.
- Look for a relationship between room preference and location.

Unfortunately, these options for further investigation are beyond the scope of this investigation.

The assignment will continue by providing an analysis of the existing computer rooms and will try to find a relationship between number of computers and floor space needed.

The information gathered suggests that a minimum of 21 computers is required and 24 computers would be desirable.

A suitable room must now be selected. Before this can be done, a relationship between room size and number of computers in the room should be found. The method selected is to measure the existing computer rooms.

The table on the following page shows floor area, computers and m^2 per computer.

> You should show your calculations, eg $56/36 = 1.\dot{5}$. You could draw a scale diagram for the room to show how you found the floor area.

Analysis of floor space in existing computer rooms.

Room	Floor area (to nearest m²)	Number of computers	m² per computer (floor area ÷ computers)
1	56	36	1.5̇
18	12	6	2
27	39	24	1.625
30	45	30	1.5
42	15	8	1.875
48	35	24	1.4583̇
Total	202	98 ←	

This should be 128

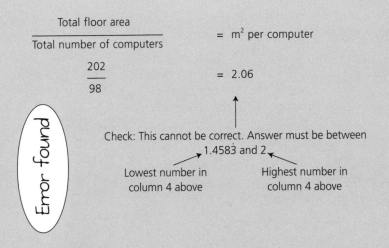

$$\frac{\text{Total floor area}}{\text{Total number of computers}} = \text{m}^2 \text{ per computer}$$

$$\frac{202}{98} = 2.06$$

Check: This cannot be correct. Answer must be between 1.4583̇ and 2.

Lowest number in column 4 above

Highest number in column 4 above

Error found

Correction

$$\frac{202}{128} = 1.578125 \text{ m}^2 \text{ per computer}$$

$$\simeq 1.58 \text{ m}^2 \text{ (rounded to 3 significant figures)}$$

Approximately **1.58 m²** of floor space is needed for each computer.

The minimum, maximum and average floor space area per computer can be used to estimate the required floor space for 21 and 24 computers.

Number of computers	Minimum area per computer (1.4583 m²)	Maximum area per computer (2 m²)	Mean average area per computer (1.58 m²)
21	30.6 m²	42 m²	33.2 m²
24	35 m²	48 m²	37.9 m²

A further check can be carried out by placing the information from the existing computer rooms onto a scatter diagram.

A line of best fit may then be drawn and if the equation of the line of best fit is calculated this will provide a formula connecting floor area and number of students (computers).

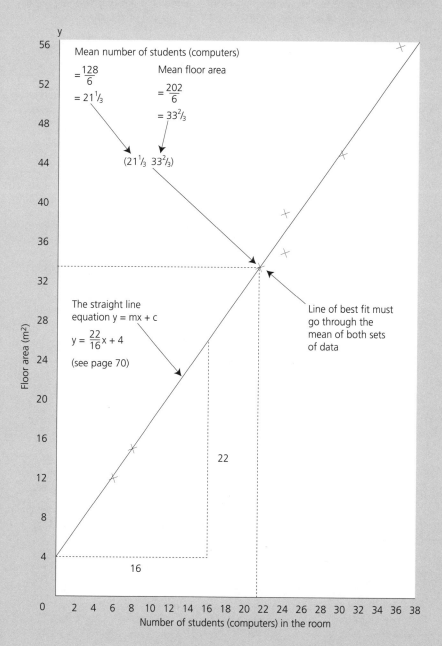

Mean number of students (computers)

$= \frac{128}{6}$

$= 21\frac{1}{3}$

Mean floor area

$= \frac{202}{6}$

$= 33\frac{2}{3}$

$(21\frac{1}{3} \quad 33\frac{2}{3})$

The straight line equation $y = mx + c$

$y = \frac{22}{16}x + 4$

(see page 70)

Line of best fit must go through the mean of both sets of data

22

16

Floor area (m²)

Number of students (computers) in the room

The equation of the line of best fit produces an equation linking floor area in m² to the number of computers in the room. The equation of the line of best fit is:

$$y = \frac{22}{16}x + 4$$

Where y = floor area in m², x = number of computers (students)

This equation can be used to find the floor area if the number of computers is known. The formula can be rearranged to find the number of computers if we know the floor area. (See also *Rewriting formulae*, page 66.)

ie
$$y = \frac{22}{16}x + 4$$

$$y - 4 = \frac{22}{16}x$$

$$\frac{16}{22}(y - 4) = x$$

$$x = \frac{16}{22}(y - 4)$$

$$\text{Computers} = \frac{16}{22}(\text{Floor area} - 4)$$

Check the formulae work

We know from the scatter diagram that eight computers need 15 m² floor space. Check:

$$y = \frac{22}{16}x + 4 \qquad\qquad x = \frac{16}{22}(y - 4)$$

$$y = \frac{22}{16}(8) + 4 \qquad\qquad x = \frac{16}{22}(15 - 4)$$

$$y = 15 \qquad\qquad x = \frac{16}{22}(11)$$

$$x = 8$$

This shows that both formulae are correct and the formulae produce the same answers as the conversion graph (see page 51) and the scatter diagram (see page 49).

The line of best fit can be used to produce a conversion graph for converting number of computers (students) and floor area.

Conversion graph for finding the floor area required for number of students (computers)

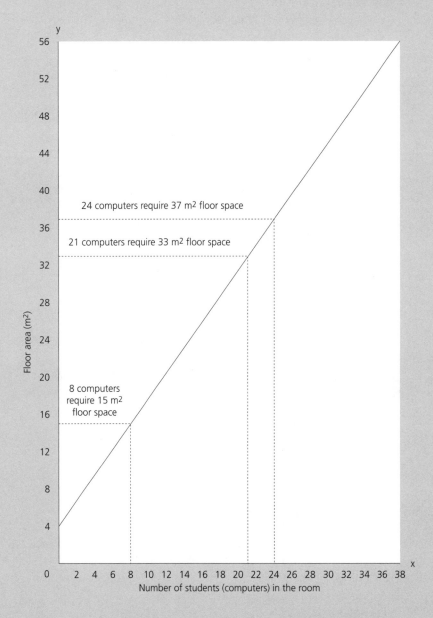

24 computers require 37 m² floor space

21 computers require 33 m² floor space

8 computers require 15 m² floor space

Floor area (m²)

Number of students (computers) in the room

The conversion graph shows that eight computers require 15 m² floor space. This agrees with the formula.

The conversion graph shows:

- 21 computers require 33 m² floor space.
- 24 computers require 37 m² floor space.

The computer room will need to have about 37 m² floor space (it could be larger). It will then take 24 computers. This suggests a room size (minimum):

$$6 \text{ m} \times 6 \text{ m} = 36 \text{ m}^2$$
$$7 \text{ m} \times 5 \text{ m} = 35 \text{ m}^2$$
$$8 \text{ m} \times 4.5 \text{ m} = 36 \text{ m}^2$$
$$9 \text{ m} \times 4 \text{ m} = 36 \text{ m}^2$$

Measuring all of the possible rooms would take a very long time. A large pace is about 1 m. Pacing rooms will establish whether they are suitable. If they are, exact measurements can be taken.

A shortlist of eight rooms was produced. Technicians and 20 teachers were asked their opinions and Room 8 was selected.

Reasons for selection were:

- Ease of conversion.
- Suitable size.
- Located close to the sixth form common room.
- Centrally located for teachers.
- A 'comfortable' room.

The next stage is to design the computer desktop area, ie the 'footprint'.

The 'footprint'

The footprint is the desk area for each computer station. It contains monitor, tower, keyboard, speakers, mouse pad.

Scale 1 cm represents 10 cm

1   :   10

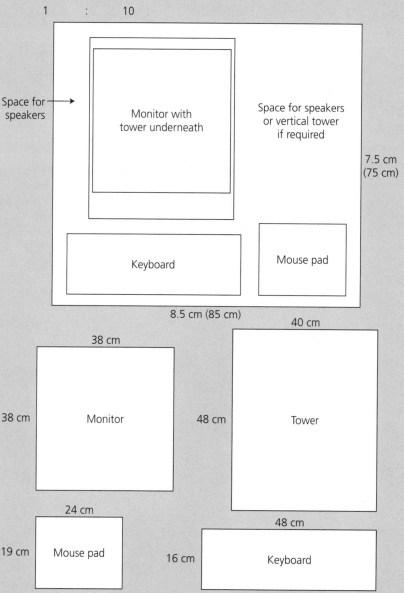

Plan for designing the computer room

1   Measure the computer room.

2   Choose an appropriate scale to fit onto your graph paper.

3   The actual assignment used the following scale:

2 cm represents 1 m.

This is a scale of   2   :   100

This simplifies to   1   :   50

(Unfortunately, this scale would not fit onto the page in this book so the example uses the more complicated scale. Advice: Use a simple scale.)

The example uses 8 cm represents 5 m.

This is a scale of   8   :   500

This simplifies to   1   :   62.5

4   a   Draw a scale diagram of the intended computer area.

   b   Draw scale diagrams of the computer stations. If you need 24 computer diagrams, draw 24 and cut them out.

5   Try arranging the small computer diagrams in the room until you find the best arrangement. (Remember to leave room for students to walk between the seats and room for the teacher, printers, etc.)

Scale 8 cm represents 5 m

8	:	500
1	:	62.5

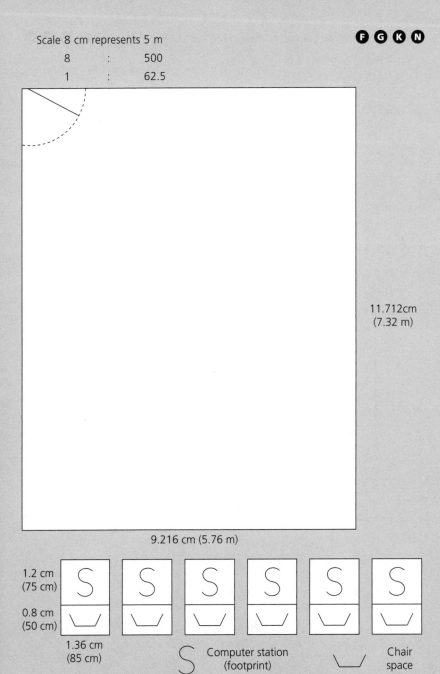

11.712cm
(7.32 m)

9.216 cm (5.76 m)

1.2 cm
(75 cm)

0.8 cm
(50 cm)

1.36 cm
(85 cm)

S Computer station
(footprint)

Chair
space

This is the finished plan of the new computer room.

F G K N O

Scale 8 cm represents 5 m

8 : 500

1 : 62.5

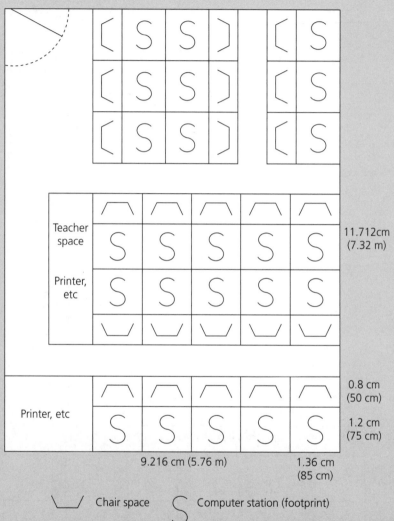

11.712cm
(7.32 m)

Teacher space

Printer, etc

0.8 cm
(50 cm)

Printer, etc

1.2 cm
(75 cm)

9.216 cm (5.76 m)

1.36 cm
(85 cm)

⌐⌐ Chair space   S Computer station (footprint)

Part 3

Revision notes

Estimating

Rounding to one significant figure (1 sig fig):

    3725   → 4000   Round to one figure, then add noughts to the

    28.63 → 30   decimal point. Do **not** add noughts after the

    421.3 → 400   decimal point.

Note 421.3 does not become 400.0

    0.038 → 0.04   Significant figures are counted from the first

    0.724 → 0.7   non-zero number.

    0.0306 → 0.03

Example

Estimate $\dfrac{38.04 + 41.13}{39162 \times 0.0191}$ by rounding each number to 1 significant figure.

Method $\dfrac{40 + 40}{40000 \times 0.02}$ = $\dfrac{80}{800}$ = $\dfrac{1}{10}$ or 0.1

Questions

1   Round 721.68 to 2 significant figures.

2   Round 0.07818 to 3 significant figures.

3   Estimate $\dfrac{49193 \times 0.0402}{40.01 + 9.89}$

Answers

1 720

2 0.0782

3 $\dfrac{50000 \times 0.04}{40 + 10}$ = $\dfrac{2000}{50}$ = 40

Standard form

Standard form is used to write very large and very small numbers.

5.36×10^4

Means move the decimal point
4 places to the right

$5\overset{\frown}{3}\overset{\frown}{6}\overset{\frown}{0}\overset{\frown}{0}$ = 53 600

8.31×10^{-3}

Means move the decimal point
3 places to the left

$0\overset{\frown}{0}\overset{\frown}{0}831$ = 0.00831

Questions

1 Write 8.4×10^3 as an ordinary number.

2 Write 3.24×10^{-2} as an ordinary number.

3 Write 3820 in standard form.

4 Write 0.00236 in standard form.

5 $(7.3 \times 10^8) \div (6.4 \times 10^{-7})$

In standard form a number is written in the form $a \times 10^b$
Where a is a number between 1 and 10 and b is an appropriate power of 10.

Using a calculator with numbers in standard form

Use the [EXP] or [EE] key

Example $3.82 \times 10^4 \times 4.26 \times 10^6$

Calculator keys:

[3] [.] [8] [2] [EXP] [4] [x]
[4] [.] [2] [6] [EXP] [6] [=]

The calculator display shows
1.62732^{11}
This means 1.62732×10^{11}

Answers

1 $8\overset{\frown}{4}\overset{\frown}{0}\overset{\frown}{0}$ = 8400

2 $0\overset{\frown}{0}\overset{\frown}{0}324$ = 0.0324

3 Note: In standard form, the decimal point is always after the first whole number.

$3\overset{\frown}{8}\overset{\frown}{2}0$ The decimal point has moved 3 places to the left.
We write the number in standard form as 3.82×10^3.

4 $0.00\overset{\frown}{2}\overset{\frown}{3}6$ The decimal point has moved 3 places to the right.
We write the number in standard form as 2.36×10^{-3}.

5 [7] [.] [3] [EXP] [8] [÷] [6] [.] [4] [EXP] [7] [+/-] [=]   Answer 1.140625×10^{15}

Common error:
Do not put [x] [1] [0] into your calculator. [EXP] does this.

Another common error is to write 1.140625^{15}.
This will lose marks. You must write 1.140625×10^{15}.

Ratio

You use ratio every day of your life. A simple example is making a glass of orange squash. You use undiluted orange and water in the ratio 1 : 4

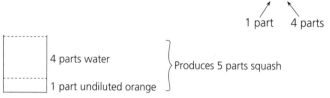

1 part   4 parts

4 parts water
1 part undiluted orange } Produces 5 parts squash

How many litres of squash can be made with a three-litre bottle of undiluted orange?

The ratio is   undiluted orange   water   squash

                      1   :   4   ⟶   5
                  one part   four parts   five parts

One part is 3 litres. Therefore five parts is 5 x 3 = 15 litres.

Questions

1   A man leaves £5000 in his will. The money is to be divided between his three sons Adam, Ben and Carl in the ratio 2:3:5. How much does each son receive?

2   This is a recipe for soup for four people: 800 ml water, 2 tomatoes, 100 g beef, 8 g salt.

    How much of each ingredient should you use for:
    a   two people?   b   six people?

3   Simplify these ratios:

    a   4:18   b   30:45

Answers

1   Adam receives   2 parts
    Ben receives   3 parts
    Carl receives   5 parts
    _____
    Total   10 parts   10 parts is £5000. Therefore 1 part is £500.

    Adam receives   2 parts   = £1000 (ie 2 x 500)
    Ben receives   3 parts   = £1500
    Carl receives   5 parts   = £2500

2   a   Two people will need half the ingredients: 400 ml water, 1 tomato, 50 g beef and 4 g salt
    b   Six people will need one and a half times the ingredients: 1200 ml water, 3 tomatoes, 150 g beef, 12 g salt

3   a   4:18, divide both sides by 2 ⟶ 2:9   b   30:45, divide both sides by 15 ⟶ 2:3

Scale and scale drawing

A scale of   1 : 20 000   means

1 cm on the map   represents   20 000 cm on the ground.

Example

The scale of a map is 1:400 000.

a   The distance between the towns of Benton and Cadnam is 7 cm on the map. What is the actual distance between these towns?

     7 x 400 000 = 2 800 000 cm

     = 28 000 m

     = 28 km

b   Hardon is 12 km from Farnham. What is the distance on the map?

     12 km = 12 000 m = 1 200 000 cm

     1 200 000 ÷ 400 000 = 3 cm

Question

The scale of a map is 1:1 000 000.

a   The distance between Hanwell and Stoke is 15 cm on the map. What is the actual distance?

b   The distance between Melksham and Trowton is 127 km. What is the distance on the map?

Answers

a   15 x 1 000 000 = 15 000 000 cm
     = 150 000 m
     = 150 km

b   127 km = 127 000 m = 12 700 000 cm
     12 700 000 ÷ 1 000 000 = 12.7 cm

Ratio for length, area and volume

Look at this:

Note: Common error, 1 m² does not equal 100 cm². Be very careful when converting units of area and volume.

The two squares are identical.
The area of A is 1 m². The area of B is 10 000 cm².

Let us see why this happens:

side 2 cm   side 3 cm

Ratio of sides (length)	x:y	ie	2:3	
Ratio of areas	x^2:y^2	ie	2^2:3^2 →	4:9
Ratio of volumes	x^3:y^3	ie	2^3:3^3 →	8:27

Note: If you are given the area ratio, you can find the length ratio by taking the square root.
If you are given the volume ratio, you can find the length ratio by taking the cube root.

Example

A map is drawn to a scale of 4 cm represents 10 km.
The area of a lake on the map is 20 cm². What is the area of the real lake?

Length ratio is   4 cm : 10 km
Area ratio is $(4 \text{ cm})^2$: $(10 \text{ km})^2$ → 16 cm² : 100 km²
(divide by 16 to find 1 cm³)   1 cm² : 6.25 km²
          20 cm² : 125 km²   Answer 125 km²

or you could use the scale factor method ie 20 x $(^{10}/_4)^2$ = 125 km²

Questions

1 Cube A has a side of 3 cm. Cube B has a side of 5 cm.

   a What is the ratio of their lengths?

   b What is the ratio of their areas?

   c What is the ratio of their volumes?

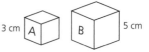

2 A map is drawn to a scale of 2 cm represents 5 km. A forest has an area of 60 km². What is the area of the forest on the map?

Answers
1 a 3:5   b 3^2:5^2 → 9:25   c 3^3:5^3 → 27:125
2 Length ratio 2 cm : 5 km
      Area ratio $(2 \text{ cm})^2$: $(5 \text{ km})^2$ →   4 cm² : 25 km²
                Therefore   0.16 cm² : 1 km²
                          9.6 cm² : 60 km²   Answer 9.6 cm²

Percentages

To calculate one number as a percentage of another number you always **divide**.

Example

284 people out of 800 wore glasses. Write this as a percentage.

> 284 out of 800 means 284 ÷ 800
> Then multiply by 100 to find the percentage,
> ie 284 ÷ 800 x 100 = 35·5%
> An alternative is to use the ⎡ **%** ⎤ key on your calculator.

Calculator keys: [**2**] [**8**] [**4**] [**÷**] [**8**] [**0**] [**0**] [**%**]   Answer 35.5%

Note: With some calculators you may have to press [**INV**] or [**SHIFT**] [**%**]

With some calculators you may have to press [**=**] at the end.

Questions

1   A man earns £250 per week. He receives a £4 increase. What percentage increase is this?

2   A TV normally costs £400. In a sale this price is reduced to £340. Calculate the percentage reduction.

Answers

1   4 ÷ 250 x 100 = 1.6%   or [**4**] [**÷**] [**2**] [**5**] [**0**] [**%**]   = 1.6%

2   First calculate the reduction. £400 – £340 = £60
You always use the original price, ie £400

60 ÷ 400 x 100 = 15%   or [**6**] [**0**] [**÷**] [**4**] [**0**] [**0**] [**%**]   = 15%

You always **divide** if you want the answer to be %.

Percentages and fractions

You have to be able to work out percentages. For example, shops often have sales with 20% off. If you cannot do percentages, you cannot work out the sale price.

> To find 6%, multiply by 0.06
>
> To calculate a 6% increase, multiply by 1.06 (ie 1 + 0.06)
>
> To calculate a 12% decrease, multiply by 0.88 (ie 1 − 0.12)
>
> To calculate $^2/_3$, multiply by $^2/_3$
>
> To calculate a $^2/_3$ increase, multiply by $1^2/_3$ (ie 1 + $^2/_3$)
>
> To calculate a $^2/_3$ decrease, multiply by $^1/_3$ (ie 1 − $^2/_3$)

Examples

1   A man earns £12 000 per annum. He receives a 4% increase each year. How much does he earn after five years?

Method: 12 000 x 1.04 x 1.04 x 1.04 x 1.04 x 1.04 = £14 599.83
    A shortcut is: 12 000 x 1.04^5 = £14 599.83

2   A television costs £200 + 17.5% VAT. What is the total cost?
    200 x 1.175 = £235

This is a common examination question:

A television costs £235 including 17.5% VAT. Calculate the cost before VAT was added. £235 is 117.5%. We need to find 100%. It is Example 2 reversed.
235 ÷ 1.175 = £200

Questions

1   A car is bought for £15 000. It depreciates by 9% each year. How much is it worth after three years? (Give your answer to the nearest £.)

2   Decrease 48 by $^1/_3$ 3   Find 8% of 20.

Answers

1   15 000   x   0.91   x   0.91   x   0.91   =   £11 304

to find the   to find the   to find the
value after   value after   value after
one year   two years   three years

The calculation can be shortened   15 000 x $(0.91)^3$

Calculator keys: [1] [5] [0] [0] [0] [x] [0] [.] [9] [1] [x'] [3] [=]

2   Decrease by $^1/_3$ means multiply by (1 − $^1/_3$) = $^1/_3$ 48 x $^2/_3$ = 32
3   Find 8% means multiply by 0.08 ⟶ 0.08 x 20 = 1.6

Using algebra

Examples

Given a = 2, b = 3, c = 4, work out the following:

1 ab   2 abc   3 $\frac{1}{4}$ab

4 (a + b)c   5 a(b + c)

Method

1 ab means a x b   2 abc means a x b x c   3 $\frac{1}{4}$ab means $\frac{1}{4}$ x a x b

                 2 x 3   2 x 3 x 4 $\frac{1}{4}$ x 2 x 3

            Answer = 6   Answer = 24   Answer = 1.5

4 (a +b)c means (a + b) x c   5 a(b + c) means a x (b + c)

                 (2 + 3) x 4   2 x (3 + 4)

Calculator keys: Calculator keys:

$\boxed{(}$ $\boxed{2}$ $\boxed{+}$ $\boxed{3}$ $\boxed{)}$ $\boxed{x}$ $\boxed{4}$ $\boxed{=}$ $\boxed{2}$ $\boxed{x}$ $\boxed{(}$ $\boxed{3}$ $\boxed{+}$ $\boxed{4}$ $\boxed{)}$ $\boxed{=}$

Answer = 20   Answer = 14

Questions

1 $A = \frac{1}{2}BH$ Find A when B = 8 and H = 4

2 $P = 2(L + W)$ Find P when L = 6 and W = 4

3 $D = \dfrac{A + E}{BC}$ Find D when A = 20, B = 2, C = 5 and E = 40

Answers

1 A   = $\frac{1}{2}$ x B x H   2   P = 2 x (L + W)

          = $\frac{1}{2}$ x 8 x 4   = 2 x (6 + 4)

          = 16   Calculator keys:

                                    $\boxed{2}$ $\boxed{x}$ $\boxed{(}$ $\boxed{6}$ $\boxed{+}$ $\boxed{4}$ $\boxed{)}$ $\boxed{=}$

                                    Answer = 20

3 D = $\dfrac{A + E}{BC}$

          = $\dfrac{(20 + 40)}{(2 \times 5)}$

Calculator keys: $\boxed{(}$ $\boxed{2}$ $\boxed{0}$ $\boxed{+}$ $\boxed{4}$ $\boxed{0}$ $\boxed{)}$ $\boxed{\div}$ $\boxed{(}$ $\boxed{2}$ $\boxed{x}$ $\boxed{5}$ $\boxed{)}$ $\boxed{=}$

Answer = 6

Rewriting formulae

A variety of techniques is shown.

Look at this:		$\sqrt{16} = 4$	and	$4^2 = 16$
	therefore	$16 = 4^2$		$4 = \sqrt{16}$
This is how it works in formulae:		$\sqrt{C} = D$	and	$E^2 = H$
	therefore	$C = D^2$		$E = \sqrt{H}$

Questions

The following questions show several useful techniques. In each question, make A the subject.

1 $\sqrt{A} = B$

2 $A2 = B$

3 $3C \sqrt{A} = B$

4 $C = B + A$

5 $C = B - A$

6 $C = \dfrac{A}{B}$

7 $C = \dfrac{B}{A}$

8 $AB + C = D$

9 $3B = \dfrac{Y}{2A} - 7$

10 $3B = \dfrac{Y-7}{2A}$

11 $V = \frac{1}{3}\pi r^2 h$ Make r the subject.

Answers

1 $\sqrt{A} = B$

   $A = B^2$

2 $A2 = B$

   $A = \sqrt{B}$

3 $3C \sqrt{A} = B$

   $\sqrt{A} = \dfrac{B}{3C}$

   $A = \left(\dfrac{B}{3C}\right)^2$

4 $C = B + A$

   $B + A = C$

   $A = C - B$

5 $C = B - A$

   $C + A = B$

   $A = B - C$

6 $C = \dfrac{A}{B}$

   $\dfrac{A}{B} = C$

   $A = BC$

7 $C = \dfrac{B}{A}$

   $AC = B$

   $A = \dfrac{B}{C}$

8 $AB + C = D$

   $AB = D - C$

   $A = \dfrac{D - C}{B}$

9 $3B = \dfrac{Y}{2A} - 7$

   $3B + 7 = \dfrac{Y}{2A}$

   $A(3B + 7) = \dfrac{Y}{2}$

   $A = \dfrac{Y}{2(3B + 7)}$

10 $3B = \dfrac{Y-7}{2A}$

   $3AB = \dfrac{Y-7}{2}$

   $A = \dfrac{Y-7}{2(3B)}$

   $A = \dfrac{Y-7}{6B}$

11 $V = \frac{1}{3}\pi r^2 h$

   $3V = \pi r^2 h$

   $\left(\dfrac{3V}{\pi h}\right) = r^2$

   $r = \sqrt{\left(\dfrac{3V}{\pi h}\right)}$

Using algebraic formulae

Example

Find D given   a = 3.2   c = 2.1

$$D = \sqrt{\left(\frac{3a - 2c}{a + c}\right)}$$

Method

First write the question replacing the letters with numbers

$$D = \sqrt{\left(\frac{3 \times 3.2 - 2 \times 2.1}{3.2 + 2.1}\right)}$$

Work out everything in the brackets.

Remember to put brackets and the start and end of each line.

$$\sqrt{\left(\frac{3 \times 3.2 - 2 \times 2.1}{3.2 + 2.1}\right)}$$

Calculator keys:

$$\boxed{\sqrt{\ }}\ \boxed{(}\ \boxed{(}\ \boxed{3}\ \boxed{\times}\ \boxed{3}\ \boxed{.}\ \boxed{2}\ \boxed{-}\ \boxed{2}\ \boxed{\times}\ \boxed{2}\ \boxed{.}\ \boxed{1}\ \boxed{)}\ \boxed{\div}$$

$$\boxed{(}\ \boxed{3}\ \boxed{.}\ \boxed{2}\ \boxed{+}\ \boxed{2}\ \boxed{.}\ \boxed{1}\ \boxed{)}\ \boxed{)}\ \boxed{=}$$

Answer = 1.0093898…

Question

Calculate the value of r given V = 90, h = 6 and V = $^{1}/_{3}\pi r^2 h$

Answer

First rewrite the formula making r the subject (see question 11 on page 62).

$$r = \sqrt{\left(\frac{3V}{\pi h}\right)} \quad r \qquad\qquad = \sqrt{\left(\frac{3 \times 90}{\pi \times 6}\right)}$$

Calculator keys:

$$\boxed{\sqrt{\ }}\ \boxed{(}\ \boxed{(}\ \boxed{3}\ \boxed{\times}\ \boxed{9}\ \boxed{0}\ \boxed{)}\ \boxed{\div}\ \boxed{(}\ \boxed{\pi}\ \boxed{\times}\ \boxed{6}\ \boxed{)}\ \boxed{)}\ \boxed{=}$$

Answer = 3.78 (approx)

Expansion of brackets

$a^3 \times a^4 = (a \times a \times a) \times (a \times a \times a \times a) = a^7$. Here are some rules to help you.

Indices (powers)

$a^3 \times a^4 = a^7$ If it is multiplication, **add** the powers: $3 + 4 = 7$

$a^8 \div a^6 = a^2$ If it is division, **subtract** the powers: $8 - 6 = 2$

$(a^5)^3 = a^{15}$ **Multiply** the powers: $5 \times 3 = 15$

$5a^4 \times 3a^6 = 15a^{10}$ **Multiply** the whole numbers and **add** the powers.

$8a^3 \div 2a^8 = 4a^{-5}$ **Divide** the whole numbers and **subtract** the powers.

Note:	$y^{-3} = \dfrac{1}{y^3}$	$5a^2$ means $5 \times a \times a$ $(5a)^2$ means $5a \times 5a = 25a^2$	$\sqrt[5]{y} = y^{1/5}$

Expansion of brackets

Example: $5y^3(3y^4 + 2ay)$ this means $5y^3 \times 3y^4 + 5y^3 \times 2ay = 15y^7 + 10ay^4$

Questions

1   $3a^5 \times 2a^4 =$

2   $5a^6 \times 2a =$

3   $3a^2cy^3 \times 4ac^5y^{-5} =$

4   $12a^3cd^8 \div 3ac^3d^2 =$

Expand the following:

5   $5(2a - 3)$

6   $3a(5 - 6a)$

7   $4y^6(2y^3 + 4y^2)$

8   $-3(a^3 + 2y^2)$

9   $4a^3b^2cd^2(3ab^4 - 6ac^3d)$

10   $(3a + 2)(5a - 3)$

11   $(6a - 7)(4a - 3)$

12   $(4y - 3)(7y + 6)$

13   $(6a - 4)^2$

Answers

1   $6a^9$

2   $10a^7$ (**Note:** $2a$ means $2a^1$)

3   $12a^3c^6y^{-2}$

4   $4a^2c^{-2}d^6$

5   $5(2a - 3)$
    $10a - 15$

6   $3a(5 - 6a)$
    $15a - 18a^2$

7   $4y^6(2y^3 + 4y^2)$
    $8y^9 + 16y^8$

8   $-3(a^3 + 2y^2)$
    $-3a^3 - 6y^2$

9   $4a^3b^2cd^2(3ab^4 - 6ac^3d)$
    $12a^4b^6cd^2 - 24a^4b^2c^4d^3$

10   $(3a + 2)(5a - 3)$
    $3a(5a - 3) + 2(5a - 3)$
    $15a^2 - 9a + 10a - 6$
    $15a^2 + a - 6$

11   $(6a - 7)(4a - 3)$
    $6a(4a - 3) - 7(4a - 3)$
    $24a^2 - 18a - 28a + 21$
    $24a^2 - 46a + 21$
    Note: $-7 \times -3 = 21$

12   $(4y - 3)(7y + 6)$
    $4y(7y + 6) - 3(7y + 6)$
    $28y^2 + 24y - 21y - 18$
    $28y^2 + 3y - 18$
    Note: $-3 \times 6 = -18$

13   $(6a - 4)^2$
    This means:
    $(6a - 4)(6a - 4)$
    $6a(6a - 4) - 4(6a - 4)$
    $36a^2 - 24a - 24a + 16$
    $36a^2 - 48a + 16$

Simultaneous equations: Solving using algebra

There are quicker ways but here is a method for solving all simultaneous equations. It will work every time in the same way.

Question

Solve the simultaneous equations:

$$4x - 5y = 2$$
$$3x - 2y = 5$$

Answer

Make the numbers in front of the 'x' the same.

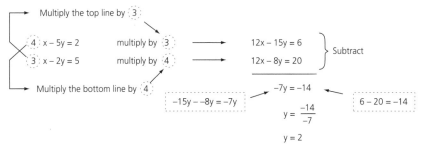

Multiply the top line by 3

$4x - 5y = 2$ multiply by 3   ⟶ $12x - 15y = 6$

$3x - 2y = 5$ multiply by 4   ⟶ $12x - 8y = 20$ } Subtract

Multiply the bottom line by 4

$-15y - -8y = -7y$

$-7y = -14$ $6 - 20 = -14$

$$y = \frac{-14}{-7}$$

$$y = 2$$

Substitute y = 2 into one of the original equations

$$4x - 5y = 2$$
$$4x - 5 \times 2 = 2$$
$$4x - 10 = 2$$
$$4x = 2 + 10$$
$$4x = 12$$
$$x = 12 \div 4$$
$$x = 3$$

Answer: x = 3, y = 2

Now check by substituting x = 3 and y = 2 in the other original equation

$$3x - 2y = 5$$
$$3 \times 3 - 2 \times 2 = 5$$
$$9 - 4 = 5$$

This is just a check. If you are short of time in an exam, you can miss it out.

Sometimes the question is shown like this:
Solve the simultaneous equations 5x = 13 − 2y and 3y = 15 − 3x
First write each question like this:

x terms		y terms	=	number
5x	+	2y	=	13
3x	+	3y	=	15

Now proceed as above.

The straight line equation y = mx + c

You can use this method to find a formula from a line of best fit on a scatter diagram (see sample project page 49.) We can find the equation of a straight line by calculating the gradient and where the line crosses the y-axis. You must learn 'y = mx + c'.

This is the gradient   This is where the line crosses the y axis

$$y = mx + c$$

$$m = \frac{\text{distance up}}{\text{distance across}}$$

If m is negative, it is $\frac{\text{distance down}}{\text{distance across}}$

Examples

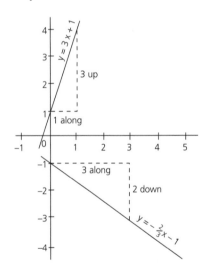

1   y = 3 x + 1
        m   c

c = +1   means that the line crosses the y axis at +1

$m = 3 = \frac{3}{1} \rightarrow \frac{\text{3 up the y axis}}{\text{1 along the x axis}}$

2   y = $-\frac{2}{3}$ x − 1
        m   c

c = −1   means that the line crosses the y axis at −1

$m = -\frac{2}{3} \rightarrow \frac{\text{2 down the y axis}}{\text{3 along the x axis}}$

Question

What is the equation of the line which passes through the points (1,2) and (3,1)?

Answer

Mark the points (1,2) and (3,1).
Draw a straight line through the points.

The equation of the line is   y = mx + c
                m = $-\frac{1}{2}$
                c = 2.5
                y = $-\frac{1}{2}$ x + 2.5

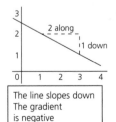

The line slopes down
The gradient
is negative

Note:

If the line slopes up, the gradient (m) is positive.

If the line slopes down, the gradient (m) is negative.

Speed, time and distance graphs

You need to be able to read information from graphs.

This graph shows the journey made by a car. What is the speed at 0900?

Note: The question may use the word velocity instead of speed.

Note:
The gradient gives the speed or velocity

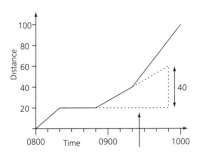

Answer:
Speed = 40 km/h

Make this line exactly one hour. Form a right-angled triangle (dotted lines). The height of the triangle will be the speed in kilometres per hour.

Questions

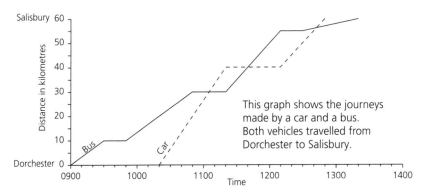

This graph shows the journeys made by a car and a bus. Both vehicles travelled from Dorchester to Salisbury.

1 a Between which times did the bus travel fastest?
   b How did you decide?

2 Describe what happened at 11.40 am.

3 How many times did the car pass the bus?

4 How long did the car stop for?

5 What was the speed of the bus on the first part of its journey?

6 What was the speed of the car at 12.30 pm?

Answers
1 a 11.20 and 12.10   b The steeper the graph, the faster the bus.
2 The bus passed the car.   3 Twice   4 50 minutes
5 20 km/h   6 30 km/h

Enlargement

Enlargement means making bigger or smaller. There are several methods of enlarging. The advantage of the method shown is that it can be used for enlargement by a whole number scale factor and a fractional scale factor.

Question

Enlarge the triangle ABC by a scale factor of 2. Centre of enlargement is the point (2,1).

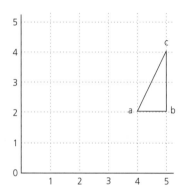

Answer

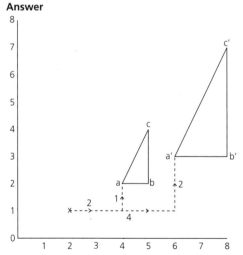

Count the distance from the centre of enlargement to each point

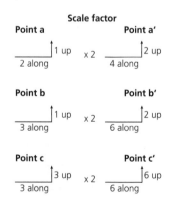

Note: Always count from the centre of enlargement.

Enlargement by a fractional scale factor

The method of enlargement used here is almost identical to that on page 72.

Question

Enlarge the triangle by a scale factor of $^2/_3$. Centre of enlargement is the point (1,1).

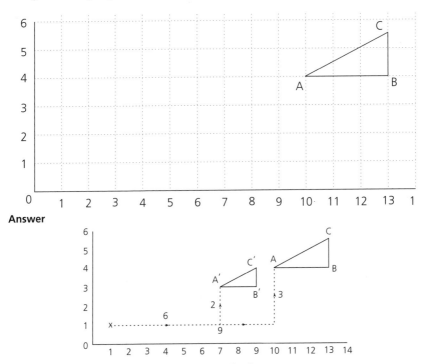

Answer

Count the distance from the centre of enlargement to each point.

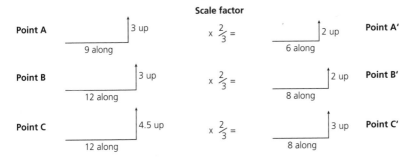

Converting one metric unit to another

Metric units are easy to convert, you always multiply or divide by 10, 100 or 1000.

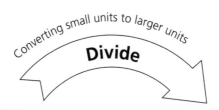

Converting small units to larger units

Divide

Length
10 millimetres (mm) = 1 centimetre (cm)
100 centimetres (cm) = 1 metre (m)
1000 metres (m) = 1 kilometre (km)

You must learn this information

Mass
1000 grams (g) = 1 kilogram (kg)
1000 kilograms (kg) = 1 tonne (t)

Capacity
1000 cubic centimetres (cc) = 1 litre (l)
1000 millilitres (ml) = 1 litre (l)
100 centilitres (cl) = 1 litre (l)
10 millilitres (ml) = 1 centilitre (cl)

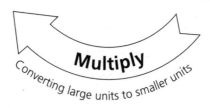

Multiply

Converting large units to smaller units

Questions

1   Convert 524 centimetres into metres.
2   Convert 3.56 tonnes into kilograms.

Note: 1 cm^3 = 1 cc = 1 ml

Answers
1   524 ÷ 100 = 5.24 metres
2   3.56 x 1000 = 3560 kilograms

Accuracy of measurement

If we count objects or people (ie discrete data), we can get an exact number. If we take a measurement of length, mass, capacity or time (continuous data), the measurement may not be exact. Lengths are often given to the nearest centimetre. This means a possible error of half a centimetre in either direction.

Example

If the length of a desk is given as 1.3 m, this indicates that the length is approximately 1.3 m. The measurement may be inaccurate.

To calculate the minimum possible value:

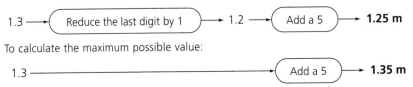

To calculate the maximum possible value:

Therefore, if the length is given as 1.3 m, this means the actual length lies between 1.25 m and 1.35 m inclusive.

Questions

1   A book has a mass of 2.18 kilograms. What are the minimum and maximum possible masses of the book?

2   The length of a blackboard is given as 2.80 m. What are the minimum and maximum possible lengths of the blackboard?

3   The length of a room is given as 7 m, correct to the nearest 0.5 m. What are the minimum and maximum possible lengths?

4   Which is more accurate: 6.2 m or 6.20 m? Explain your answer.

Answers

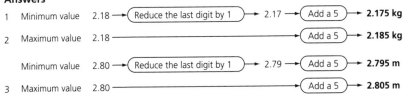

This question is slightly different. It gives you the level of accuracy, ie 0.5 m.
Method: Halve the level of accuracy, ie half of 0.5 m is 0.25 m.
Minimum length is 7 m − 0.25 m = 6.75 m
Maximum length is 7 m + 0.25 m = 7.25 m

4   6.2 m is correct to one decimal place, 6.20 m is correct to two decimal places. 6.20 is more accurate.

Compound measures

Speed and density are compound measures because we give the speed in m/s or km/h, ie two units. If mass is given in kg and volume in m^3, the density will be given in kg/m^3.

The following formulae must be memorised:

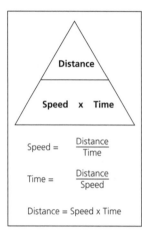

Speed = $\dfrac{Distance}{Time}$

Time = $\dfrac{Distance}{Speed}$

Distance = Speed x Time

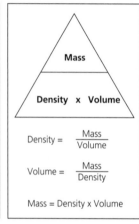

Density = $\dfrac{Mass}{Volume}$

Volume = $\dfrac{Mass}{Density}$

Mass = Density x Volume

You may have used these formulae in Science.

Suppose you want to know what speed equals. Cover up speed. This shows:

Therefore Speed = $\dfrac{Distance}{Time}$

You will use this method in trigonometry (that is sin, cos, tan) on page 83.

Questions

1 A car takes 8 hours 10 minutes to travel 343 kilometres. Calculate the average speed.

2 A man walks at a speed of 24 metres in 10 seconds. Calculate his speed in kilometres per hour.

3 Mass is given in g, volume is given in cm^3. What units are used for density?

Answers

1 Decide if you require the answer in kilometres per hour or kilometres per minute.
If you choose kilometres per hour, change 8 hours 10 minutes into hours.
10 minutes is $^{10}/_{60}$ of an hour.
Therefore 8 hours 10 minutes = $8^{10}/_{60}$ hours.
Speed = Distance = $\dfrac{343}{8^{10}/_{60}}$ = 42 kilometres per hour.
       Time

2 24 metres in 10 seconds
(multiply by 6)   144 metres in 1 minute
(multiply by 60)   8640 metres in 60 minutes (ie 1 hour)
(divide by 1000)   8.64 kilometres in 1 hour
                     The speed is 8.64 kilometres per hour.

3 g/cm^3

Circles

You must know how to use all of the formulae shown. Carefully note the two common errors at the bottom of the page.

Circumference of a circle = $2\pi r$
(this means 2 x π x radius)

Area of a circle = πr^2
(this means π x radius x radius)

Volume of a cylinder = $\pi r^2 h$
(this means π x radius x radius x height)

Cylinder

A common error: Always ask yourself, does the question give the **radius** or the **diameter**? In any examination, about 20% of the candidates will confuse radius and diameter. Be careful you are not one of them. To avoid this, before using any circle formulae ask "Do we have the radius?". If the answer is "Yes", continue. If not, find the radius. The **radius** is **half** of the **diameter**.

Questions

1   Find the circumference and area of a circle radius 6 cm.

2   Find the circumference and area of a circle diameter 8 cm.

3   Find the radius of a circle, area 40 m².

4   Find the volume of a cylinder diameter 80 cm, height 1.2 m.

Answers

1   Do we have the radius? Yes. Continue.

Circumference = 2 x π x radius	Area = π x radius x radius
= 2 x π x 6	= π x 6 x 6
= 37.7 cm	= 113 cm²

2   Do we have the radius? No. First we have to find the radius. The radius is 4 cm.

Circumference = 2 x π x radius	Area = π x radius x radius
= 2 x π x 4	= π x 4 x 4
= 25.1 cm	= 50.3 cm²

Question 4 alternative answer
If you want the answer in m³, you **must** convert to metres **before** you multiply:
= π x 0.4 m x 0.4 m x 1.2 m
= 0.603 m³

3   $A = \pi r^2$ (look back to *Rewriting formulae*, page 56).
Make r the subject:

$$\frac{A}{\pi} = r^2$$

$$\sqrt{\left(\frac{A}{\pi}\right)} = r$$

$$\sqrt{\left(\frac{40}{\pi}\right)} = r \quad \text{Calculator keys:}$$

[√] [( ] [4] [0] [÷] [π] [ )] [=]

3.57 m = r

Common error: Never try to convert squared or cubed units. **Look:**

603000 cm³ does **not** equal 6030 m³

4   Do we have the radius? No. First halve the diameter to find the radius. The radius is 40 cm.

Volume = π x radius x radius x height
= π x 40 x 40 x 120
= 603186 cm³
= 603000 cm³

Common error: You cannot use mixed units, ie cm and m. Change 1.2 m into 120 cm

Calculating length, area and volume

You need to understand length, area, volume, perimeter and know the units each is measured in. You must know what is meant by cross-section, prism, parallelogram, trapezium, and how to use the formulae. (These formulae will be given on the examination paper.)

> **Remember:** Perimeter is the distance around a shape.
> Area is length x width (always measured in units², eg mm², cm², m²).
> Volume is length x width x height (always measured in units³, eg mm³, cm³, m³).

You are expected to know how to use these formulae:

Area of a triangle
= $^1/_2$ x base x perpendicular height (PH)

Area of a parallelogram
= base x perpendicular height

Area of a trapezium
= $^1/_2$ (a + b) x perpendicular height

Volume of a cuboid
= length x width x height

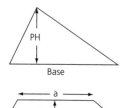

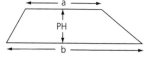

Questions

1   Find   a   the perimeter
            b   the area of this shape.

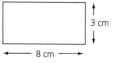

2   Find the area.

3   Find the area.

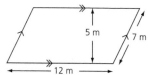

4   Find the area.

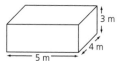

5   Find the volume.

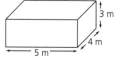

Answers

1   a 8 cm + 3 cm + 8 cm + 3 cm = 22 cm   b   8 cm x 3 cm = 24 cm²
2   $^1/_2$ x 7 cm x 6 cm = 21 cm²   3   12 m x 5 m = 60 m² (**Note:** 7 m is not used)
4   Area = $^1/_2$ x (12 cm + 20 cm) x 8 cm   5   5 m x 4 m x 3 m = 60 m³
         = $^1/_2$ x 32 cm x 8 cm
         = 128 cm² (**Common error:** 128 cm² does **not** equal 1.28 m²)

Prism

A prism is any solid shape with a uniform cross-section, ie same shape at each end.

Cross-section

The cross-section is the shape that goes all through a prism, ie the shaded parts in these shapes.

Example

Find the volume of this prism:

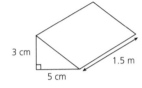

Volume = cross-sectional area x length

First find the cross-sectional area

Area of a triangle = $\frac{1}{2}$ base x height = $\frac{1}{2}$ x 5 x 3 = 7.5 cm²

Note: The length is 1.5 m. This must be changed into centimetres, ie 150 cm.

Volume = 7.5 cm² x 150 cm = 1125 cm³

Question

Find the area and perimeter of this shape:

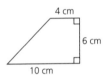

Answer

The formula to find the area of a trapezium is $\frac{1}{2}$ (a+b) x perpendicular height.

Area = $\frac{1}{2}$ (4 + 10) x 6
     = $\frac{1}{2}$ (14) x 6
     = 7 x 6
     = 42 cm²

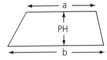

To find the perimeter we must use Pythagoras' theorem to find the missing side (see *Pythagoras' theorem*, page 81).

$x^2 = 6^2 + 6^2$
$x^2 = 36 + 36$
$x^2 = 72$
$x = \sqrt{72}$
$x = 8.49$ cm

Perimeter = 4 + 6 + 10 + 8.49 = 28.49 cm

Cuboid

Volume of a cuboid = length x width x height

Volume of a cuboid = 6 cm x 3 cm x 4 cm
= 72 cm³

Note: Area is in units², eg cm², m²
Volume is in units³, eg cm³, m³

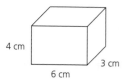

Questions

1 a Find the area.
  b Find the perimeter.

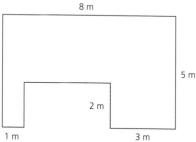

2 This is a diagram of a garden with a lawn and a path around the edge.
The path is 2 m wide.

Find the area of the path.

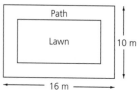

Answers

1 a Split the shape into three parts.
     Area = 32 m²
  b 8 m + 5 m + 3 m + 2 m
    + 4 m + 2 m + 1 m + 5 m = 30 m

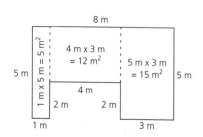

2 Find the area of the large rectangle = 10 x 16 = 160 m²
  Find the area of the small rectangle = 6 x 12 = 72 m²
  Take away   = 88 m²

> **Note:** It is 6 x 12
> A common error is 8 x 14.
> Remember 2 m wide at both ends.

Pythagoras' theorem

When you know the lengths of two sides of a right-angled triangle you can use Pythagoras' theorem to find the third side.

Pythagoras' theorem: $a^2 + b^2 = c^2$ (where c is the longest side)

Note: The longest side is always opposite the right angle.

Examples

Find x

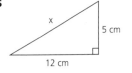

$$5^2 + 12^2 = x^2$$
$$25 + 144 = x^2$$
$$169 = x^2$$
$$\sqrt{169} = x$$
$$13 \text{ cm} = x$$

Find y

$$y^2 + 8^2 = 10^2$$
$$y^2 = 10^2 - 8^2$$
$$y^2 = 100 - 64$$
$$y^2 = 36$$
$$y = \sqrt{36}$$
$$y = 6 \text{ cm}$$

To find the **long** side.	To find either **short** side.
Square both numbers. **Add** them together. Take square root of result.	Square both numbers. **Subtract** the smaller from the larger. Take square root of result.

Questions

1 Find x.

2 Find the height of this isosceles triangle:

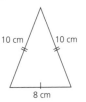

Answers

1 To find a short side:
Square both numbers 12^2 7^2
Subtract   144 – 49 $h^2 + 4^2$
(Note: Big number – small number.) h^2
Square root $\sqrt{95}$
Answer x =   9.75 m

2 An isosceles triangle can be split into two right-angled triangles.
$$= 10^2$$
$$= 10^2 - 4^2$$
$$h^2 = 100 - 16$$
$$h^2 = 84$$
$$h = \sqrt{84}$$
$$h = 9.165 \text{ cm}$$

Trigonometry: Finding an angle

Remember the rules shown. If you are finding an angle, you press the TOP LEFT key on your calculator (ie [shift] [INV] or [2nd F]. If you are finding a side you do **not** press the TOP LEFT key on your calculator.

Information similar to this will be given on your examination paper.

Note: This only works for right-angled triangles.

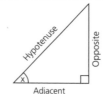

$SIN = \dfrac{OPP}{HYP}$

$COS = \dfrac{ADJ}{HYP}$

$TAN = \dfrac{OPP}{ADJ}$

To find an angle

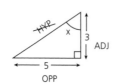

Method

1 Label the triangle.
   Hypotenuse = the longest side, opposite the right angle
   Opposite = opposite the angle being used
   Adjacent = next to the angle being used

2 Cross out the side not being used.
   In this question HYP.

3 Look at the formulae in the box at the top.
   Which uses OPP and ADJ?

4 $TAN = \dfrac{OPP}{ADJ} = \dfrac{5}{3}$

5 Calculator keys

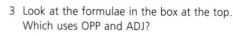

↑
Top left key on most calculators; it will show Shift, Inv or 2nd Function

The answer displayed should be
59.0362... ⟶ 59.0°

Question

Find x

Answer

$COS = \dfrac{ADJ}{HYP} = \dfrac{3}{8}$

$= 67.975687... ⟶ 68.0°$

Trigonometry: Finding a side

We have used this method before (see page 76).

SIN = $\frac{OPP}{HYP}$ → | OPP / SIN X HYP |

COS = $\frac{ADJ}{HYP}$ → | ADJ / COS X HYP |

TAN = $\frac{OPP}{ADJ}$ → | OPP / TAN X ADJ |

Cover up what you want and the formula will appear,

eg cover up OPP

SIN X HYP   OPP = SIN x HYP

or cover up HYP

OPP / SIN   HYP = $\frac{OPP}{SIN}$

To find a side

Method

1 Label the triangle.
   Hypotenuse = the longest side, opposite the right angle
   Opposite = opposite the angle being used
   Adjacent = next to the angle being used

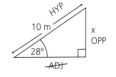

2 You need the side you are finding (x).
   You need the side you know (10 m).
   Cross out the side not being used. In this question ADJ.

3 Look at the formulae above. Which uses OPP and HYP?

4 We need OPP, cover up OPP to find the formula:

SIN X HYP   OPP = SIN x HYP

OPP = SIN28° x 10

5 Calculator keys

[SIN] [2] [8] [x] [1] [0] [=]

This should give you an answer 4.6947.. ——→ 4.69 m

Note: If this does not work, ask your teacher to show you how to work your calculator.

Question

Find x

Answer

COS = $\frac{ADJ}{HYP}$ → | ADJ / COS X HYP |

Cover up HYP to find the formula

HYP = $\frac{ADJ}{COS}$

HYP = $\frac{8}{\cos 40°}$

Calculator keys:

 [8] [÷] [cos] [4] [0] [=]

Answer x = 10·4 m

Trigonometry: Solving problems

This diagram shows a man at the top of a cliff looking down at a boat.

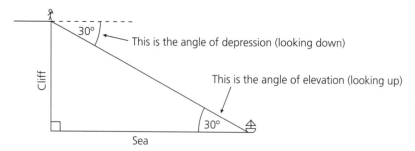

30°

This is the angle of depression (looking down)

This is the angle of elevation (looking up)

Cliff

30°

Sea

Note: The angle of depression from the top of the cliff is equal to the angle of elevation from the boat.

Angles of depression and angles of elevation are measured from the horizontal.

Answering questions

1 Read the question carefully.

2 It may help to visualise what is required. You can use objects such as pencils, rubbers, rulers to make a model of what is required.

3 Draw a diagram. Remember you need a right-angled triangle.

4 Read the question again. Check that your diagram is correct.

Question

Sarah is flying a kite. The string is 80 m long and the angle of elevation is 32°. How high is the kite?

Answer
Draw a diagram.

HYP

80 m

?

OPP

32°

ADJ

OPP

SIN x HYP

Cover up OPP

OPP = SIN x HYP
    = SIN32° x 80
    = 42.4 m

Tables and graphs

Information can be obtained from graphs. You need to know how to extract the information you need.

This is a conversion graph for changing miles into kilometres.

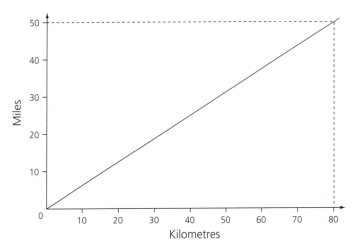

Examples

1   The distance from Exeter to Dorchester is 50 miles. How far is this in kilometres?

   Method: Find 50 miles on the graph. Draw a dotted line from the 50 mile mark to the conversion line. Draw a dotted line from the point it meets the conversion line to the kilometres scale. The distance in 80 kilometres.

2   Convert 300 kilometres into miles.

   Method: The scale does not have 300 kilometres. Use 30 kilometres instead. 30 is about 19 miles. Therefore 300 kilometres is about 190 miles.

Questions

1   Convert 50 kilometres into miles.

2   Convert 30 miles into kilometres.

Answers
1   31 or 32 miles   2   48 kilometres
Your answers need not be exact.

Frequency tables and frequency diagrams

Continuous data is data which can have any value, eg distance between two places, height of a person. The height of a person can be measured to any degree of accuracy. A person could be 1.783642 m tall.

Discrete data is data which can only have certain values, eg the number of people in a room can only have whole number values. You cannot have 3.2 people in a room.

If you are asked to collect data, you must choose an appropriate method – usually a survey or an experiment. You must record your data and then present it in tables, diagrams and graphs.

Questions

The following are the times taken by 20 people to complete a jigsaw. The times are in minutes:

8.62, 28.4, 48.13, 30.1, 26.03, 47.42, 36.01, 25.23, 22.6, 29.97, 18.63, 30.00, 42.73, 38.62, 20.01, 19.99, 27.6, 16.32, 8.7, 12.58.

a Record the information in a frequency table. Choose suitable equal class intervals.

b Show this information in a frequency diagram.

Answers

a A common error is:

Minutes
0–10
10–20
20–30

Where would you record 20?
In the 10–20 or 20–30?

Minutes	Tally	Frequency
0–under 10	II	2
10–under 20	IIII	4
20–under 30	LHT II	7
30–under 40	IIII	4
40–under 50	III	3

Advice: Always add the frequency total. There are 20 people, ➞ 20 therefore, the frequency must add up to 20.

b

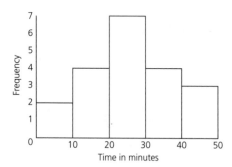

Comparing data

Sometimes you will be asked to compare two sets of data. If you are comparing, you must write about the similarities and differences of **both** sets of data.
A frequency polygon is a graph produced by joining up points with straight lines.

Questions

The heights of 20 boys and 20 girls aged 16 are shown in this table:

Height (cm)	Number of boys	Number of girls
140–149	–	1
150–159	1	3
160–169	6	8
170–179	8	6
180–189	4	2
190–199	1	–

1   Present the data in a frequency polygon.

2   Compare the distributions and comment on your findings.

Answers
1

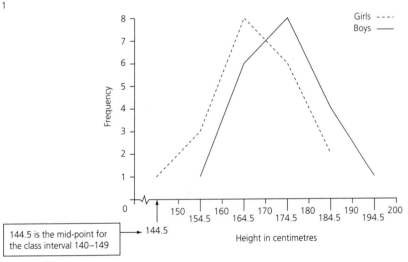

144.5 is the mid-point for the class interval 140–149 → 144.5

2   The frequency polygon shows that boys aged 16 are generally taller than girls of the same age.

Averages

There are three main types of average – mean, median and mode. Many students get them mixed up and that is just throwing away marks.

Median and mode are measures of average. The **median** is the middle number when the numbers are placed in order. The **mode** is the most common number.

Questions

1   Find the median and mode of these numbers:

2, 3, 5, 3, 2, 4, 2.

2   Find the median of these numbers:

7, 3, 10, 2.

3   The masses of boxers in a tournament are given in kilograms:

65, 63, 68, 64, 69, 68, 63, 64, 67, 69, 63, 61, 63, 67, 60.

Find the median and the mode

Answers

1   First place the numbers in order of size.

3 is the middle number, therefore, the median is 3

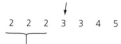

There are more 2s than any other number, therefore, the mode is 2

2   Place the numbers in order

2   3   7   10

The median is between 3 and 7

$$\frac{3+7}{2} = \frac{10}{2} = 5$$

The median is 5.

3   Place the numbers in order: 60, 61, 63, 63, 63, 63, 64, 64, 65, 67, 67, 68, 68, 69, 69.
The median is 64.
The mode is 63.

The **mean** is the most useful average because it uses all of the data. The mean is sometimes called the arithmetic mean.

The **range** is the difference between the largest and smallest numbers.

Example

a   Find the mean of: 16, 18, 11, 19, 17.   b   Find the range.

Method

a   Add the numbers, then divide by how many numbers there are.

$$\frac{16 + 18 + 11 + 19 + 17}{5} = \frac{81}{5} = 16.2$$

b   The range is $19 - 11 = 8$

Questions

1   There are four children in a room. Their ages are: 16, 14, 13 and 15.

   a   What is the mean of their ages?

   b   What is the range?

2   This table shows the number of letters delivered to houses in a street:

Letters	0	1	2	3	4	5
Number of houses	3	2	6	7	0	2

   Calculate the mean number of letters delivered to each house.

3   The mean of four numbers is 7. The numbers are 5, 3, 8 and x. Find x.

Answers

1   a $\frac{16 + 14 + 13 + 15}{4} = \frac{58}{4} = 14.5$

   b $16 - 13 = 3$

2   This is a very common exam question.

> Two **common errors** are $\frac{0+1+2+3+4+5}{6} = 2.5$ and $\frac{0+1+2+3+4+5}{3+2+6+7+0+2} = \frac{15}{20} = 0.75$

Mean $= \frac{\text{Total number of letters}}{\text{Total number of houses}} = \frac{(0 \times 3) + (1 \times 2) + (2 \times 6) + (3 \times 7) + (4 \times 0) + (5 \times 2)}{3 + 2 + 6 + 7 + 0 + 2} = \frac{45}{20} = 2.25$

3   The mean of four numbers is 7. Therefore, the total is $4 \times 7 = 28$.

$$5 + 3 + 8 + x = 28$$
$$16 + x = 28$$
$$x = 12$$

Comparing two sets of data

The mean, median or mode can be used as a measure of average.

If a question asks you to compare two lists of information, you must write about the differences between the lists.

If you have a choice, it is easiest to compare by using the mean. It is most difficult to compare by using the mode.

Question

These are the Maths test results (out of ten marks) for Jenny and Paul:

Test	1	2	3	4	5	6	7	8	9	10
Jenny's marks	8	6	8	5	4	6	7	6	8	4
Paul's marks	9	10	9	8	3	4	1	8	9	10

Use the range and mean to compare their marks. Who is better at Maths and why?

Answer

Jenny's range of marks is 8 − 4 = 4
Paul's range of marks is 10 − 1 = 9

> You should compare the ranges

Jenny's marks have a smaller range. This suggests that she is more consistent than Paul. Jenny always gains a satisfactory mark. Paul scores some very good marks and some very poor marks.

Jenny's mean mark is $\frac{62}{10}$ = 6.2

Paul's mean mark is $\frac{71}{10}$ = 7.1

The mean marks suggest Paul is slightly better at Maths, but the range suggests that he is very good in some areas and very poor in other areas.

If a test question asks you who is better, you can state either person, but you must give a reason based on the range and mean, median or mode.

Grouped data

Information is often grouped. We can estimate the median, mean and range.

Questions

This table shows the number of cars using a car park over a period of 100 days:

Number of cars	0–99	100–199	200–299	300–399	400–500
Frequency	5	18	30	27	20

1   What is the modal class?

2   Estimate the median.

3   Estimate the mean.

Answers

1   The modal class is the class with the highest number. In this question it is 200–299 cars.

2   There are 100 days. The median is the middle day when arranged in order of size. The question asks for an estimate, therefore we can assume that the median is the 50th day.

  5 + 18 = 23. Therefore, there are 23 days with less than 200 cars.
  5 + 18 + 30 = 53. Therefore, there are 53 days with less than 300 cars.
  The 50th day is towards the high end of the 200–299 class.
  A good estimate of the median would be about 290 cars.

3   This question is similar to question 2 on page 89.
  The mean is found by first multiplying the mid-value of each class by the frequency. The question asks for an estimate, therefore, we can use 50, 150, 250, 350 and 450 as the mid-values.

$$\frac{(5 \times 50) + (18 \times 150) + (30 \times 250) + (27 \times 350) + (20 \times 450)}{100}$$

$$= \frac{250 + 2700 + 7500 + 9450 + 9000}{100}$$

$$= \frac{28900}{100}$$

  The mean number of cars is about 289.

Cumulative frequency

We can use cumulative frequency curves to compare data.

Questions

This table shows the marks of pupils in an exam:

Mark	Frequency
6–15	3
16–25	10
26–35	14
36–45	28
46–55	20
56–65	5

1   What is the range of the marks?

2   Draw a cumulative frequency diagram

3   What is the median mark?

4   What is the upper quartile?

5   What is the lower quartile?

6   What is the interquartile range?

7   Pupils need 50 or over for an A grade. How many A grades were awarded?

Answers

1   The range is 65 – 6 = 59.

2   First complete a cumulative frequency column.

Mark	Frequency	Cumulative frequency
6–15	3	3
16–25	10	3 + 10 = 13
26–35	14	3 + 10 + 14 = 27
36–45	28	3 + 10 + 14 + 28 = 55
46–55	20	3 + 10 + 14 + 28 + 20 = 75
56–65	5	3 + 10 + 14 + 28 + 20 + 5 = 80

Note: Points are plotted at the maximum value of the class interval, eg the 46–55 interval is plotted at (55,75) not (50,75).

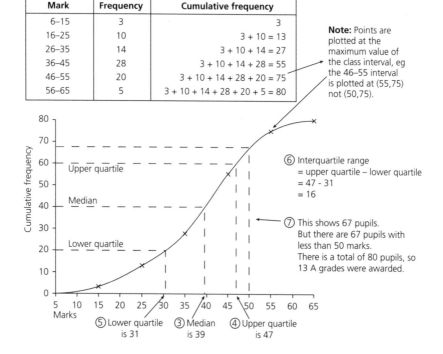

⑥ Interquartile range
= upper quartile – lower quartile
= 47 - 31
= 16

⑦ This shows 67 pupils. But there are 67 pupils with less than 50 marks. There is a total of 80 pupils, so 13 A grades were awarded.

⑤ Lower quartile is 31

③ Median is 39

④ Upper quartile is 47

Using cumulative frequency diagrams to compare distributions

Question

Two different makes of light bulbs were compared. The cumulative frequency diagrams show the number of hours the bulbs lasted:

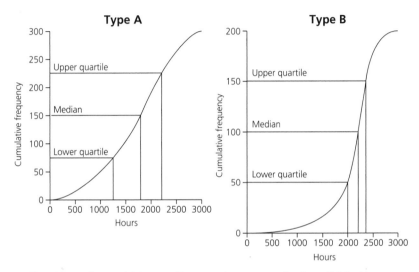

Use the median and interquartile range to compare the two distributions.

Answer

Different numbers of bulbs were used in the tests but the median and interquartile range allow comparisons between the two types of bulb. The interquartile range measures the range of the middle half of the distribution.

The median of bulb A is about 1800 hours.
The median of bulb B is about 2200 hours.
This implies that bulb B is better because the median bulb lasts 400 hours longer.

The interquartile range of bulb A is about (2200 – 1250) 950 hours.
The interquartile range of bulb B is about (2400 – 2000) 400 hours.

The middle half of bulb B is bunched together, ie steeper curve.
The middle half of bulb A is more spread out.

The information suggests that bulbs of type B are more consistent and have a longer lifetime.

Scatter diagrams

Scatter diagrams are used to find relationships (or correlation) between two sets of data.

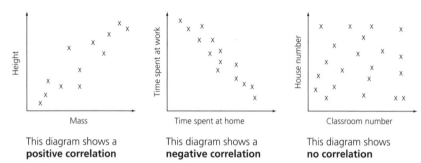

This diagram shows a
positive correlation

This diagram shows a
negative correlation

This diagram shows
no correlation

A positive correlation indicates that as one quantity increases so does the other quantity. The diagram shows that, in general, taller people are heavier.

A negative correlation indicates that as one quantity increases, the other quantity decreases. The diagram shows that, in general, the more time a person spends at work, the less time they spend at home.

No correlation indicates that there is no relationship between the two quantities. The diagram shows that a house number has no connection with the classroom number.

> **Note:** Remember to use the word **correlation** in your answer.

Questions

1 Describe the relationship shown by this scatter diagram.

2 Explain the reason for this relationship.

Answers

1 Negative correlation.
 As the temperature increases, the number of hot drinks sold decreases.
 or As the temperature decreases, the number of hot drinks sold increases.
2 In hot weather, people drink fewer hot drinks.
 In cold weather, people drink more hot drinks.

Scatter diagram: Line of best fit

A line of best fit is drawn by looking at the crosses on a scatter diagram and then drawing a line. Normally there would be a similar number of crosses above the line as below the line.

Questions

1 Draw a line of best fit on this scatter diagram. This scatter diagram shows the masses of 16 pupils against their ages.

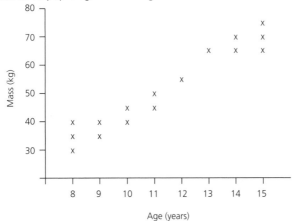

2 Use your line of best fit to estimate the mass of a 13-year-old pupil.

Answers

1 The line of best fit should be in a similar position to the line shown.

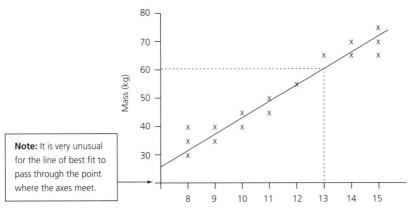

Note: It is very unusual for the line of best fit to pass through the point where the axes meet.

2 **Method:** Draw a line from 13 years to the line of best fit. Read the mass. The answer should be about 60 kg.

Pie charts

Pie charts allow us to present information. Information presented in a diagram is often easier to understand than information in a table. You will be expected to read information from pie charts and draw pie charts.

Questions

This pie chart shows how the pupils in class 3A arrive at school:

1   How many pupils walk to school?
2   What is the angle for the bus sector?
3   How many pupils attend the school?
4   Complete the car sector.

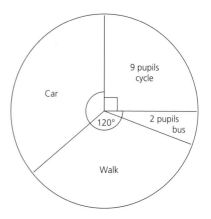

Answers

The first thing to do is find the angle for one pupil. The pie chart shows 9 pupils cycle to school. This sector is 90°.
9 pupils are represented by 90°
1 pupil is represented by 10°

1   The angle for the walk sector is 120°
    We know that 1 pupil is represented by 10°
    Therefore **12 pupils** are represented by 120°
2   2 pupils arrive by bus.
    We know that 1 pupil is represented by 10°
    Therefore 2 pupils are represented by **20°**
3   There are 360° in a circle.
    We know that 1 pupil is represented by 10°
    Therefore **36 pupils** are represented by 360°
4   The angles of a circle add up to 360°
    cycle + bus + walk + car = 360°
    90° + 20° + 120° + x = 360°
    The angle for the car sector is **130°**
    The pupils add up to 36
    cycle + bus + walk + car = 36
    9 + 2 + 12 + y = 36
    13 pupils arrive by car.

96

Drawing pie charts

Question

30 people were asked what sort of holiday they would choose. 5 said a mountain resort, 10 said a beach holiday, 7 said an activity holiday and 8 said a cruise. Show this information in a pie chart.

Answer

The first thing to do is find the angle for one person. There are 360° in a circle. The pie chart must represent 30 people.

360° ÷ 30 = 12°   Therefore 12° represents 1 person.

Holiday choice	Frequency	Multiply by 12°	Angle at the centre of the pie chart
Mountain resort	5	x 12°	60°
Beach holiday	10	x 12°	120°
Activity holiday	7	x 12°	84°
Cruise	8	x 12°	96°

How to draw the pie chart

1 Draw a circle.
   Draw a line from the centre to the edge.

2 Place the protractor on the circle.
   Place the centre of the protractor on the centre of the circle.
   Make sure 0° is on the line.
   Measure the first angle, 60°.

3 Draw a line from the centre to the edge at 60°.
   Label the sector 'Mountain resort' and write 60°.

4 Move the protractor as shown.
   Measure 120°.
   Draw a line from the centre to the edge.

5 Repeat for 84°.
   Check the remaining angle is 96°.
   Label each sector.

Do not forget: Label each sector and show the angle size.	Measure the angles carefully. If angles are not accurate, you will lose marks.

Part 4

The examination

Examination advice

Read the following advice before taking the sample examination on pages 101 to 110.

- Make sure you take the following equipment to the exam: pen, pencil, ruler, rubber, pair of compasses, protractor, and scientific calculator.
- Read all instructions.
- Read each question. Make sure you understand what you are required to do.

Students often drop pints by misreading the question!

- Show all working. Marks are given for working.
- Check your answers to make sure they are sensible.
- If you cannot do a question, move on. Return to it later.
- Make sure you answer all of the questions.
- Do not spend too much time on any single question in part 1.
- You should spend about 45 minutes on part 1 and 45 minutes on part 2.
- If you finish early, go back and check your answers.
- Learn these formulae:

$$\text{SIN} = \frac{\text{OPP}}{\text{HYP}}$$

$$\text{COS} = \frac{\text{ADJ}}{\text{HYP}}$$

$$\text{TAN} = \frac{\text{OPP}}{\text{ADJ}}$$

Pythagoras' theorem
$$a^2 = b^2 + c^2$$

Circumference of a circle $= 2\pi r$
Area of a circle $\qquad = \pi r^2$
Area of a triangle $\qquad = \frac{1}{2}$ base x height

Sample examination

Key Skills Level 3 Application of Number

A scientific calculator should be used.

Time allowed: 90 minutes

Write clearly so that your work can be easily understood.

You should show all working.

You should answer all of the questions.

There are two parts to the examination:

- Part 1: Short answer questions (25 marks).
- Part 2: Extended answer question (25 marks).

Space is allowed within this book for answering the questions in Part 1.

Part 1: Short answer questions (25 marks)

You should spend 45 minutes on Part 1.

1   The ratio of the weight (mass) of Mr Green to Mrs Green is 3:2.
    Mr Green weights 75 kg. Mrs Green diets and reduces her weight
    by 10%.

    a   What is the weight of Mrs Green after her diet?   *(2 marks)*

    b   What is the new ratio of weight of Mr Green to Mrs Green
        after her diet?   *(1 mark)*

2   Estimate the value of this calculation. You **must** show
    your working.

    $$\frac{4018 \times 0.0195}{7981 \times 0.00391}$$ *(2 marks)*

3   Mrs White receives a salary increase of 5%. After the increase
    she earns £23 142 per annum. What was her salary before
    the increase?   *(2 marks)*

4   This is a scale drawing of a lawn with a path around it. The scale is 1:400.

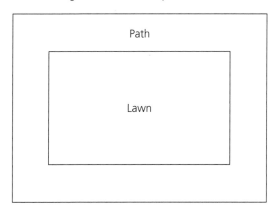

a   What is the area of the lawn in the diagram? Give your answer
    in cm². *(2 marks)*

b   What is the area of the actual lawn? Give your answer in m².   *(2 marks)*

c   What is the area of the path in the diagram? Give your
    answer in cm².   *(2 marks)*

5   Draw a scale diagram of this triangle, to a scale of 1:200

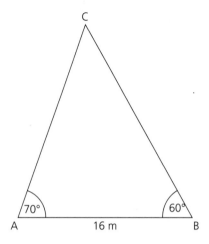

(2 marks)

6   Write these numbers in standard form:

   a   3 760 000   *(1 mark)*

   b   0.000 23   *(1 mark)*

7   A boat is 300 m from the base of a vertical cliff. The angle of
    elevation from the boat is 23°. Calculate the height of the cliff.
    Give your answer correct to the nearest metre.   *(2 marks)*

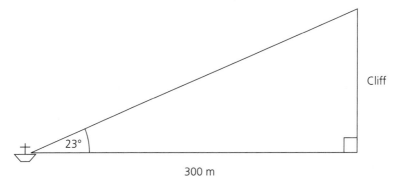

Cliff

23°

300 m

8 A population of bears is decreasing by 6% per year. In 1994, there were 20 000 bears. When the population falls below 12 000, the bears will be declared an endangered species.

a In which year would you expect the bears to be declared an endangered species? Show your working to explain your answer. *(2 marks)*

b Give a factor which could change the year in which the bears become an endangered species. *(1 mark)*

9 This table shows the number of newspapers delivered to houses
in Acasta Avenue on Sunday:

Number of newspapers	0	1	2	3	4
Number of houses	3	2	5	4	6

a Calculate the mean number of newspapers per house.　　　*(2 marks)*

b What is the modal group?　　　*(1 mark)*

Part 2: Extended answer question (25 marks)

You should spend 45 minutes on Part 2.

A group of pupils aged between 12 years and 14 years 2 months took an English test and a Maths test. The results were then standardised. The Maths marks were standardised using the table in Figure 1 (page 109). The English marks were standardised using the formula:

$$S = 4(T - 23) - \frac{8(A - 144)}{3}$$

where:

S is the standardised English mark

T is the English test mark

A is the age of the pupil given in months.

The results are shown below. The boys' marks have been standardised using the above methods:

	Name	Age in months	English test marks	English standardised marks	Maths test marks	Maths standardised marks
B O Y S	Alan	148	43	69	24	75
	Barry	150	45	72	26	75
	Carl	168	67	112	44	105
	Dave	163	52	65	33	70
	Edward	144	50	108	27	100
	Fred	153	51	88	31	90
	Gavin	157	66	137	39	120
	Harry	161	68	135	42	125
G I R L S	Ilsa	160	70		43	
	Jane	149	60		31	
	Kerry	154	58		35	
	Lyndsey	144	56		32	
	Megan	156	65		39	

Figure 1

This table may be used to convert Maths test marks into standardised marks.

Maths test marks	Age in months								
	144-146	147-149	150-152	153-155	156-158	159-161	162-164	165-167	168-170
20	65	63	61	59	57	55	53	51	49
21	70	64	62	60	58	56	54	52	50
22	75	65	63	61	59	57	55	53	51
23	80	70	64	62	60	58	56	54	52
24	85	75	65	63	61	59	57	55	53
25	90	80	70	64	62	60	58	56	54
26	95	85	75	65	63	61	59	57	55
27	100	90	80	70	64	62	60	58	56
28	105	95	85	75	65	63	61	59	57
29	110	100	90	80	70	64	62	60	58
30	115	105	95	85	75	65	63	61	59
31	120	110	100	90	80	70	64	62	60
32	125	115	105	95	85	75	65	63	61
33	130	120	110	100	90	80	70	64	62
34	135	125	115	105	95	85	75	65	63
35	135	130	120	110	100	90	80	70	64
36	135	135	125	115	105	95	85	75	65
37	135	135	130	120	110	100	90	80	70
38	135	135	135	125	115	105	95	85	75
39	135	135	135	130	120	110	100	90	80
40	135	135	135	135	125	115	105	95	85
41	135	135	135	135	130	120	110	100	90
42	135	135	135	135	135	125	115	105	95
43	135	135	135	135	135	130	120	110	100
44	135	135	135	135	135	135	125	115	105
45	135	135	135	135	135	135	130	120	110
46	135	135	135	135	135	135	135	125	115
47	135	135	135	135	135	135	135	130	120
48	135	135	135	135	135	135	135	135	125
49	135	135	135	135	135	135	135	135	130
50	135	135	135	135	135	135	135	135	135

a   Give a reason why the test marks are standardised. *(1 mark)*

b   Use *Figure 1*, page 109, to convert the Maths test marks into Maths standardised marks. The boys' results have been standardised. You should fill in the girls' Maths standardised marks. *(3 marks)*

c   Formula $S = 4(T - 23) - \dfrac{8(A - 144)}{3}$

where:

S is the English standardised mark (given to the nearest whole number)

T is the English test mark

A is the age in months.

The above formula is used to calculate the English standardised marks. Use the formula to convert English test marks into standardised marks and hence fill in the girls' English standardised marks. *(4 marks)*

d   Use the standardised marks for Maths to compare the boys and girls. Your answer should include the range for both. You should also choose and find an appropriate average (mean, median or mode) and give a reason for your choice of mean, median or mode. *(8 marks)*

e   i   Draw a scatter diagram for the boys. Plot the English standardised marks on the horizontal axis and the Maths standardised marks on the vertical axis. *(4 marks)*

     ii   Draw a line of best fit. *(2 marks)*

     iii   Describe the relationship shown by the scatter diagram. *(1 mark)*

     iv   Use your line of best fit to estimate the Maths standardised marks for a pupil who obtained an English standardised mark of 125. Draw appropriate lines on your graph to show how you found your answer. *(2 marks)*

Sample examination answers

Part 1

1 a Ratio   3:2

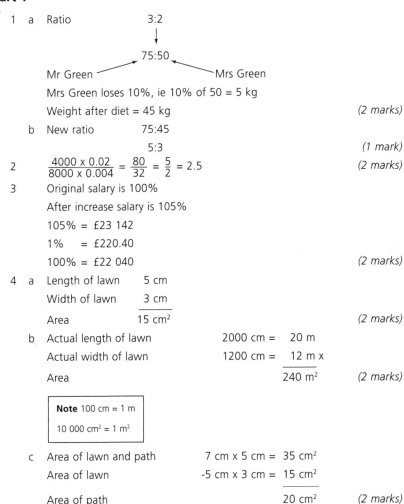

                 75:50

Mr Green   Mrs Green

Mrs Green loses 10%, ie 10% of 50 = 5 kg

Weight after diet = 45 kg   *(2 marks)*

   b New ratio   75:45

                 5:3   *(1 mark)*

2   $\dfrac{4000 \times 0.02}{8000 \times 0.004} = \dfrac{80}{32} = \dfrac{5}{2} = 2.5$ *(2 marks)*

3   Original salary is 100%

      After increase salary is 105%

      105% = £23 142

      1%   = £220.40

      100% = £22 040   *(2 marks)*

4 a Length of lawn   5 cm

      Width of lawn   3 cm

      Area   15 cm²   *(2 marks)*

   b Actual length of lawn   2000 cm =   20 m

      Actual width of lawn   1200 cm =   12 m x

      Area   240 m²   *(2 marks)*

> **Note** 100 cm = 1 m
> 10 000 cm² = 1 m²

   c Area of lawn and path   7 cm x 5 cm = 35 cm²

      Area of lawn   -5 cm x 3 cm = 15 cm²

      Area of path   20 cm²   *(2 marks)*

5

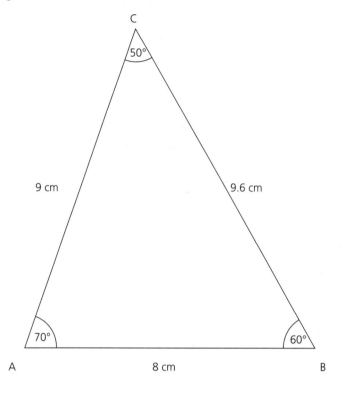

(2 marks)

6 a 3.76 x 10⁶ (1 mark)
  b 2.3 x 10⁻⁴ (1 mark)

7

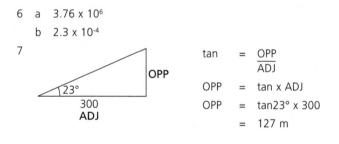

tan	=	$\frac{OPP}{ADJ}$
OPP	=	tan x ADJ
OPP	=	tan23° x 300
	=	127 m

(2 marks)

8 a There are several ways to do this question, but the easiest is trial and improvement. Each year the population reduces by 6%, ie the population is 94% of what it was the previous year.

After 1 year	20 000 x 0.94	18800	Too high
After 5 years	20 000 x 0.94 x 0.94 x 0.94 x 0.94 x 0.94 shortcut: 20 000 x $(0.94)^5$	14678	Too high
After 10 years	20 000 x $(0.94)^{10}$	10772	Too low
After 7 years	20 000 x $(0.94)^7$	12970	Too high
After 8 years	20 000 x $(0.94)^8$	12191	Too high
After 9 years	20 000 x $(0.94)^9$	11460	

Declared an endangered species in 1994 + 9 = 2003.   *(2 marks)*

   b Any valid reason. For example, disease could reduce the population more quickly. A ban on hunting could help the population to grow or reduce more slowly. Fewer bears means more food for the remaining bears, etc.   *(1 mark)*

9 a

Number of newspapers	0	1	2	3	4	Total
Number of houses	3	2	5	4	6	20
Total number of newspapers	0 x 3 = 0	1 x 2 = 2	2 x 5 = 10	3 x 4 = 12	4 x 6 = 24	48

$$\frac{\text{Total number of newspapers}}{\text{Total number of houses}} = \frac{48}{20} = 2.4$$

(2 marks)

   b The modal group is four newspapers because this is the largest group.   *(1 mark)*

Part 2

a   Test marks are standardised to compensate for the difference in ages.

or

The Maths and English tests may have different levels of difficulty or be out of different marks. Note that Alan scores 43 in English. This standardises as 69. He scores 24 in Maths. This standardises as 75. Standardised marks show he is slightly better at Maths.

or

Standardised marks allow comparison between English and Maths.

(1 mark)

b and c

Name	English standardised marks	Maths standardised marks
Ilsa	145	130
Jane	135	110
Kerry	113	110
Lyndsey	132	125
Megan	136	120

(7 marks)

d

	Range	Mean	Median
Boys	55	95	95
Girls	20	119	120

You must show the **range**. You must show either the **mean** or the **median**.

If you chose mean, your reason could be:

- It makes use of all of the data.
- It can be calculated exactly.
- Better than median because median only use middle or middle two marks.

If you chose median, your reason could be:

- Simple to calculate.
- It is not affected by very high or low values in the data.

No marks for choosing mode. If you chose mode, this was not appropriate. Mode is the largest group. The girls mode is 110. These are two of the lowest marks.

The boys' mean is considerably lower than the girls' mean. This suggests the girls are better at Maths.

The girls' range is lower than the boys'. This suggests that there is less variation in their ability, ie all similar ability. *(8 marks)*

e   Scatter diagram *(4 marks)*

Line of best fit *(2 marks)*

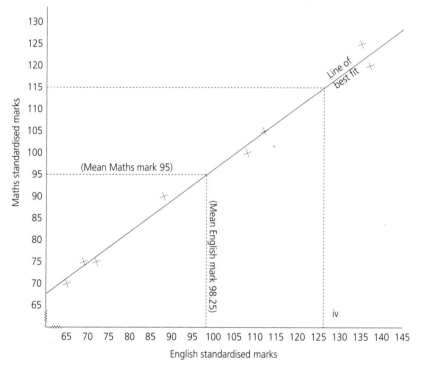

Scatter diagram showing English and Maths standardised marks for the boys. (Note line of best fit goes through the mean English mark (98.25) and the mean Maths mark (95).)

  iii Scatter diagram shows positive correlation.

     Or pupils who score high marks in English score high marks in Maths. *(1 mark)*

  iv English mark of 125. Draw line to line of best fit. Estimated Maths mark is 115. *(2 marks)*

Glossary

QCA/CCEA/ACCAC has provided the following glossary of terms used in Key Skills specifications.

Complex:
Complex subjects and materials present a number of ideas, some of which may be abstract, very detailed or require you to deal with sensitive issues. The relationship of ideas and lines of reasoning may not be immediately clear. Specialised vocabulary and complicated sentence structures may be used.

Complex activities:
The objectives or targets usually need to be agreed with others. Problems will have a number of sub-problems and will be affected by a range of factors. The tasks involved, and the relationship between them, may not be immediately clear. Situations and resources may be unfamiliar.

Complex subjects and materials:
Those that include a number of ideas, some of which may be abstract, very detailed or require you to deal with sensitive issues. The relationship of ideas and lines of reasoning may not be immediately clear. Specialised vocabulary and complicated sentence structures may be used.

Critical reflection:
This is taken to mean a deliberated process when you take time, within the course of your work, to focus on a period of your performance and think carefully about the thinking that led to particular actions, what happened and what you are learning from the experience, in order to inform what you might do in the future.

Dynamically complex work:
Work that includes activities that are interrelated, where it is likely that action in one activity will effect changes in other aspects of the work in ways that may be difficult to predict or control (eg when external changes to timescales or resources produce new problems and you have to balance technical and human demands to meet tight deadlines).

Evidence:
What you need to produce to prove you have the skills required. Examples include items you have made, written material, artwork, photographs, audio/video recordings, computer printouts of text and images, such as graphs and charts, could be used as evidence for written communication and for presenting findings in Application

of Number, as well as IT. Records of problem solving activities could include evidence of how you have worked with others, or improved you own learning and performance. Evidence can be used to back up your statements in a progress file or other record of achievement.

Extended documents: Include textbooks, reports, articles and essays of more than three pages. They may deal with straightforward or complex subjects and include images such as diagrams, pictures and charts. You are asked to read and write extended documents at Level 2 and above.

Portfolio: A file or folder for collecting and organising evidence for assessment. It should include a contents page to show where evidence for each part of the unit(s) can be found. This may be in hard copy or electronic form.

Problem: There is a problem when there is a need to bridge a gap between a current situation and a desired situation. At Levels 4 and 5, problems will be complex. They will have a number of sub-problems and will be affected by a range of factors, including a significant amount of contradictory information. They will have several possible solutions, requiring you to extend your specialist knowledge of methods and resources and adapt your strategy in working towards a satisfactory outcome.

Objectives: The purposes for working together that are shared by you and other people involved in the activity. Objectives may be those set, for example, by an organisation, your tutor, supervisor or project leader or members of your group or team.

Straightforward: Straightforward subjects and materials are those that you often meet in your work, studies or other activities. Content is put across in a direct way with the main points being easily identified. Usually, sentence structures are simple and you will be familiar with the vocabulary.

Straightforward activities: The objectives, targets or problems are given, or easily identified. It is clear how to break down the work into manageable tasks. Situations and resources are usually familiar.

Substantial activity: An activity that includes a number of related tasks, where the results of one task will affect the carrying out of the others. For example, in Application of Number a substantial activity will involve obtaining and interpreting information, using this information when carrying out calculations and explaining how the results of your calculations meet the purpose of the activity.

Strategy: A plan, for an extended period of time, that builds on what you know from past experiences and includes the development of logical steps towards achieving a specific purpose, but also has scope to adapt approach in response to feedback from others and demands resulting from changes in the wider context of your work.

Targets: The steps for helping you to achieve your personal learning or career goals. Targets should be SMART:

- **Specific** – say exactly what you need to.
- **Measurable** – say how you will prove you have met them.
- **Achievable** – be challenging, but not too difficult for you.
- **Realistic** – have opportunities and resources for meeting them.
- **Time-bound** – include deadlines.

Useful Web sites

Key Skills Support Programme
http://www.keyskillssupport.net/

QCA Web sites

Key Skills general information
http://www.qca.org.uk/nq/ks/

Key Skills specifications
http://www.qca.org.uk/nq/ks/main2.asp

Key Skills awarding bodies
http://www.qca.org.uk/nq/ks/keyskills_ab.asp

Level 3 example tests
http://www.qca.org.uk/nq/ks/example_tests_index_3.asp

Exam boards and awarding bodies

The following Web addresses are the specific pages in each exam board/awarding body dedicated to guidance and support for Key Skills.

AQA (Assessment and Qualifications Alliance)
http://www.aqa.org.uk/qual/keyskills.html

Edexcel
http://www.edexcel.org.uk/edexcel/subjects.nsf/
(httpKeySkillsHomePage)?OpenForm

OCR (Oxford Cambridge and RSA Examinations)
http://www.ocr.org.uk/schemes/keyskills/ksindex.htm

WJEC (Welsh Joint Education Committee)
http://www.wjec.co.uk/keyskills.html

CCEA (Northern Ireland Council for the Curriculum, Examinations and Assessment)
http://www.ccea.org.uk/keyskills.htm

ASDAN (Award Scheme Development and Accreditation Network)
http://www.asdan.co.uk/
(Click on 'Key Skills' on the left-hand side menu.)

City & Guilds

http://www.key-skills.org/

Organisations

DfES (Department for Education and Skills)

http://www.dfes.gov.uk/

LSC (Learning and Skills Council)

http://www.lsc.gov.uk/

UCAS (Universities and Colleges Admission Service)

http://www.ucas.ac.uk/

Resources

BBC Education: FE Key Skills

http://www.bbc.co.uk/education/archive/fe/skills/index.shtml
(This site is out of date but offers some useful exercises.)

South Yorkshire Key Skills Passport

http://www.sykeyskills.co.uk/